Letts

GCSE

VISUAL
REVISION
GUIDE

SUCCESS

QUESTIONS & ANSWERS

& ANSWERS

BIOLOGY

Author

Hannah Kingston

CONTENTS

Vertical label: **HOMEWORK DIARY**

TOPIC	SCORE
The Digestive System	/27
Help with Digestion	/29
Nutrition and Food Tests	/27
Circulation	/26
Blood	/26
Getting to the Heart of the Matter	/29
The Breathing System	/32
Respiration	/25
The Nervous System	/26
The Eye	/25
Cells	/33
Diffusion, Osmosis and Active Transport	/31
Plant and Leaf - Structure to Function	/33
Plant Senses	/22
Plant Transport and Good Health	/27
Photosynthesis	/25
The Skin	/30
The Kidneys 1	/30
The Kidneys 2	/30
Causes of Disease	/30
Defence against Disease	/28
Drugs, Solvents, Alcohol and Tobacco	/21
Hormones and Diabetes	/29
The Menstrual Cycle	/28
Variation	/22
Genetics	/33
Genetic Engineering	/33
Inherited Diseases	/27
Mitosis	/27
Meiosis and Fertilisation	/24
Genes, Chromosomes and Mutations	/24
Selective Breeding	/24
The Carbon Cycle	/32
The Nitrogen Cycle	/28
Food Chains and Webs	/22
Pyramids of Numbers and Biomass	/22
Evolution	/20
Adaptation and Competition	/23
Human Influence on the Environment	/27
Acid Rain, Pollution and the Greenhouse Effect	/24
Biotechnology	/25

EXAM HINTS

- Read the information on the front page of the exam paper. This will tell you how many questions you should answer. If you have a choice of questions, make absolutely sure that you answer questions on the topics you have studied.

- Read through all the questions that you are going to answer, then begin with the one you know best.

- Highlight the command words and make sure you answer the question. For example, does it say 'describe' or 'explain'? Does it ask for examples?

- Before the exam find out how many marks are available and how long the exam will take. Divide the number of minutes by the number of marks to work out the time available for each mark. You should find you have about 1 minute per mark.

- Use the number of marks available for each question to guide you on how many points you need to make and how much to write.

- Stick to your schedule during the exam. The first marks are the easiest to gain, so don't waste time trying to pick up extra marks when you should be moving on to the next question.

- Learn the technical biological words, and then use them in the exam. You will gain marks for the quality of your language.

THE DIGESTIVE SYSTEM

A

Choose just one answer, a, b, c or d.

1 Where are the villi found?
(a) small intestine (c) large intestine
(b) liver (d) stomach (1 mark)

2 What is bile?
(a) liquid in the stomach
(b) an enzyme
(c) a solution that helps break down fats
(d) a food droplet (1 mark)

3 What is the name of the process that moves food down the gut?
(a) absorption
(b) excretion
(c) digestion
(d) peristalsis (1 mark)

4 What are conditions like in the stomach?
(a) neutral
(b) acidic
(c) alkaline
(d) cold (1 mark)

5 What do large insoluble molecules get broken down into?
(a) large soluble molecules
(b) medium soluble molecules
(c) small soluble molecules
(d) small insoluble molecules (1 mark)

Score /5

B

Answer all parts of the questions.

1 Complete the following table by choosing the correct part of the digestive system from the list

| small intestine | stomach | liver | gall bladder | pancreas |

Function	Part of the digestive system
Where digestion is completed	
Stores bile	
Produces bile	
Produces three types of enzyme	
Produces only one type of enzyme	

(5 marks)

2 The table below list some features of three digestive juices. If a feature is correct for a digestive juice, put a tick in a appropriate box, if incorrect, put a cross.

Feature	Saliva	Gastric juice	Pancreatic juice
Slightly alkaline			
produced by the stomach			
contain a protease			
contains lipase			

(6 marks)

Score /16

C **These are GCSE-style questions. Answer all parts of the questions.**

1 The diagram below shows part of the digestive system.

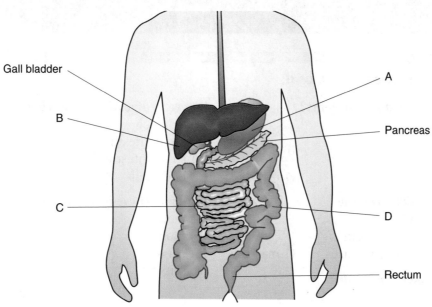

(a) Name parts A, B, C and D

A ....

B ....

C ....

D ....   (4 marks)

(b) Name one part of the digestive system where

(i) bile is produced ....

(ii) the conditions are acidic ....

(iii) carbohydrase, lipase and protease enzymes are produced

....

(iv) excess water and salts are removed ....   (4 marks)

2 Describe the function of bile in the digestion of fats.

....

....

....   (3 marks)

Score   /11

How well did you do?

0–6 correct Try again
7–13 correct Getting there
14–21 correct Good work
22–27 correct Excellent!

TOTAL SCORE   /27

**For more on this topic
see pages 4–5 of your Success Guide**

HELP WITH DIGESTION

A

Choose just one answer, a, b, c or d.

1 Which enzyme breaks down proteins?
(a) carbohydrase
(b) protease
(c) amylase
(d) lipase (1 mark)

2 Which enzyme breaks down the carbohydrate starch?
(a) amylase (c) pepsin
(b) lipase (d) protease (1 mark)

3 What are fats broken down into?
(a) glucose
(b) fatty acids
(c) amino acids
(d) fatty acids and glycerol (1 mark)

4 Where is digestion completed?
(a) stomach
(b) large intestine
(c) small intestine
(d) body cells (1 mark)

5 Which of these is not a type of tooth?
(a) incisors
(b) molars
(c) canines
(d) scissors (1 mark)

Score /5

B

Answer all parts of the questions.

1 Complete the following table by writing in the most appropriate word(s) in the blank spaces

Part of the digestive system	Enzyme used	Nutrient digested	Products
mouth	amylase		sugars
	pepsin		
small intestine		lipids	

(6 marks)

2 (a) The rate at which enzymes are digested depends on conditions. The stomach has certain conditions needed for the enzyme pepsin to work. What are they?

....

....

.... (2 marks)

(b) What happens to food that is not digested and absorbed?

....

....

.... (3 marks)

Score /16

C   **These are GCSE-style questions. Answer all parts of the questions.**

1   The diagram below illustrates digestion and absorption in the digestive system.

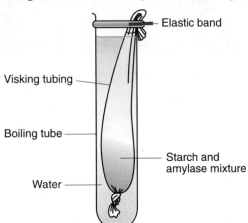

Elastic band

Visking tubing

Boiling tube

Water

Starch and amylase mixture

(a) What does the following represent?

　(i) visking tubing ....

　(ii) water ....

　(iii)liquid A ....   (3 marks)

(b) At the start, the water and liquid A were tested for starch and glucose. What were the results for the

　(i) water ....

　(ii) liquid A? ....   (2 marks)

(c) After 1 hour the water and liquid A were tested again for starch and glucose. What were the results for the

　(i) water ....

　(ii) liquid A? ....   (2 marks)

(d) Explain these results.

　...

　...

　...   (3 marks)

2 **(a)** Explain why we have to digest our food.

　...

　...

　...   (3 marks)

Score   /13

How well did you do?

0–7 correct Try again
8–14 correct Getting there
15–22 correct Good work
23–29 correct Excellent!

TOTAL SCORE   /29

For more on this topic
see pages 6–7 of your Success Guide

NUTRITION AND FOOD TESTS

A

Choose just one answer, a, b, c or d.

1 Why do we need fibre in our diet?
(a) for growth and repair
(b) for healthy bones and teeth
(c) to help food move through the system
(d) for energy   (1 mark)

2 What is the chemical test for glucose?
(a) Benedicts solution
(b) Benedict's solution and heat
(c) Biuret's solution
(d) iodine   (1 mark)

3 Why do we need protein in our diet?
(a) for growth and repair
(b) for healthy bones and teeth
(c) for energy
(d) for energy storage   (1 mark)

4 What is the chemical test for protein?
(a) Benedict's solution
(b) iodine
(c) water
(d) Biuret's solution   (1 mark)

5 What is the chemical test for starch?
(a) iodine
(b) Biuret's solution
(c) Benedict's solution
(d) ethanol   (1 mark)

Score   /5

B

Answer all parts of the questions.

1 Complete the following table of nutrients and their effects on the body by filling in the boxes with the appropriate word(s).

Nutrient	Use in body	Symptom of deficiency
Iron		anaemia
Calcium		rickets
Vitamin D	absorption of calcium	
Vitamin C		

(5 marks)

2 A balanced diet should also include carbohydrates, fats and protein. Explain why each of these nutrients is needed.

....

....

....

....

.... (3 marks)

Score   /8

C **These are GCSE-style questions. Answer all parts of the questions.**

1 The table below shows the composition of some common foods.

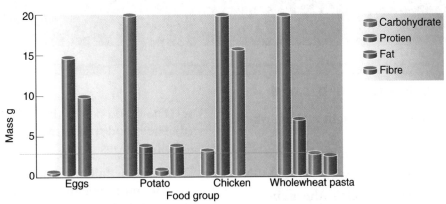

(a) Which foods would you be advised to eat to obtain more energy?

.... (1 mark)

(b) Explain your answer to (a).

.... (1 mark)

(c) Why do we need fibre in our diet? Give one effect of a lack of fibre in the diet?

....

.... (2 marks)

(d) The food groups shown above form part of a balanced diet. What other food groups make up a balanced diet.

....

.... (3 marks)

2 (a) A sample of rice was tested to see what food groups it contained.

Describe how you would test it for the following food groups and state what the positive result would be.

(i) starch ....

....

(ii) glucose ....

....

(iii) protein ....

....

(7 marks)

Score   /14

How well did you do?

0–8 correct Try again
9–15 correct Getting there
16–22 correct Good work
23–27 correct Excellent!

TOTAL SCORE   /27

For more on this topic
see pages 8–9 of your Success Guide

CIRCULATION

A Choose just one answer, a, b, c or d.

1 Once the blood enters the right atrium, where does it go next?

(a) left ventricle   (c) vena cava

(b) right ventricle   (d) left atrium   (1 mark)

2 Which of these blood vessels is the main artery of the body?

(a) aorta   (c) vena cava

(b) pulmonary artery   (d) hepatic artery

                            (1 mark)

3 Why is the human circulation called a double circulation?

(a) The blood takes twice as long as other circulations.

(b) The blood passes through each part of the body twice.

(c) The blood passes through the heart twice.

(d) The blood travels twice as fast as other circulations.   (1 mark)

4 Which of the following blood vessels delivers oxygen and nutrients to the kidneys?

(a) carotid artery

(b) renal vein

(c) jugular vein

(d) renal artery   (1 mark)

5 Which side of the heart receives oxygenated blood?

(a) left

(b) neither side

(c) right

(d) both sides   (1 mark)

Score   /5

B Answer all parts of the questions.

1 True or false?

	True	False
(a) The jugular vein transports blood from the head and neck back to the heart.	☐	☐
(b) The hepatic artery supplies the kidney with oxygen and nutrients.	☐	☒
(c) The renal artery supplies the liver with oxygen and nutrients.	☐	☐
(d) The carotid artery supplies the head and neck with oxygen and nutrients.	☐	☐

                           (4 marks)

2 Fill in the gaps.

The blood enters the heart from the vena cava into the ....

The blood then flows into the right ventricle. The right ventricle pumps the blood to the

.... via the pulmonary artery. Oxygenated blood comes back into the left atrium via

the .... The blood then leaves the heart from the

thick-walled .... into the .... to continue

its journey around the body.

                           (5 marks)

Score   /9

C

These are GCSE-style questions. Answer all parts of the questions.

The diagram shows a simplified version of the passage of oxygen around the body.

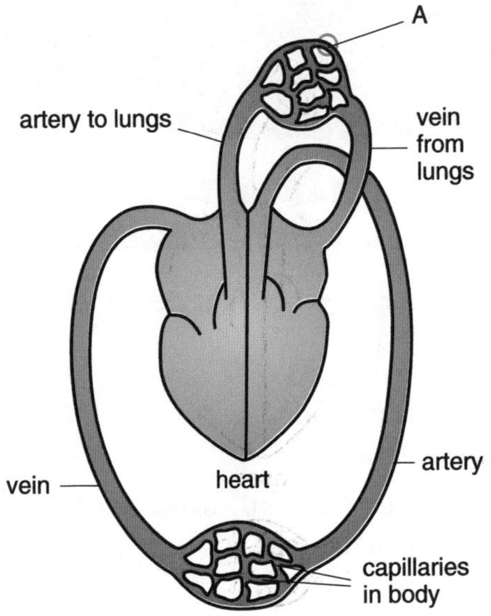

1 (a) What organ does the letter A represent?

.... (1 mark)

(b) What happens to oxygen in organ A?

.... (1 mark)

(c) What happens to the oxygen in the blood in the body organs?

.... (1 mark)

(d) Name the process by which oxygen leaves the blood.

.... (1 mark)

A

artery to lungs

vein from lungs

artery

vein

heart

capillaries in body

(e) Which of the blood vessels has the lowest concentration of oxygen? Explain why.

....

.... (2 marks)

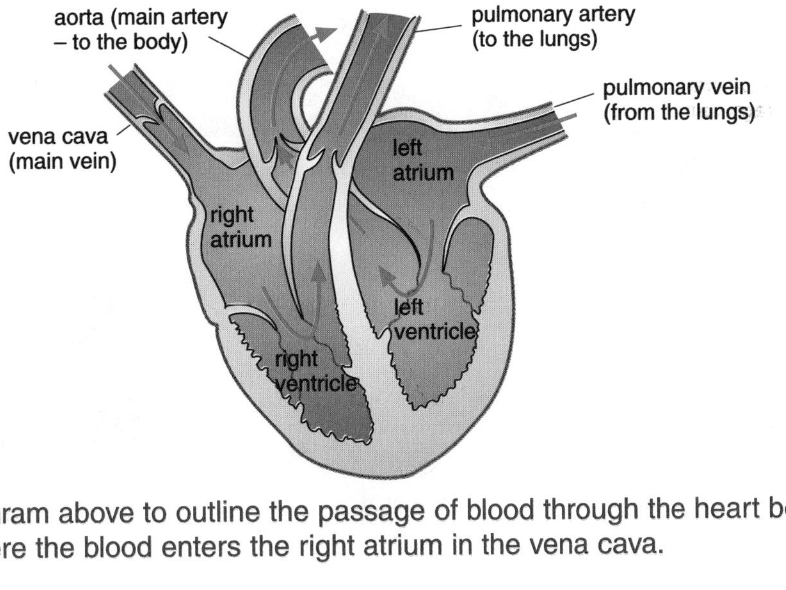

aorta (main artery – to the body)

pulmonary artery (to the lungs)

vena cava (main vein)

pulmonary vein (from the lungs)

left atrium

right atrium

left ventricle

right ventricle

2 Use the labelled diagram above to outline the passage of blood through the heart beginning and ending from where the blood enters the right atrium in the vena cava.

....

....

....

.... (6 marks)

Score   /12

How well did you do?

0–6 correct Try again
7–13 correct Getting there
14–20 correct Good work
21–26 correct Excellent!

TOTAL SCORE   **/26**

For more on this topic see pages 10–11 of your Success Guide

13

BLOOD

A

Choose just one answer, a, b, c or d.

1 Which blood cell carries oxygen?
(a) plasma
(b) red blood cells
(c) white blood cells
(d) platelets   (1 mark)

2 Which blood cell engulfs bacteria?
(a) phagocytes
(b) lymphocytes
(c) red blood cells
(d) platelets   (1 mark)

3 What is an antigen?
(a) a chemical floating around in the plasma
(b) a chemical made by white blood cells
(c) a chemical on a microbe
(d) a chemical made in the blood   (1 mark)

4 Which of the following is not dissolved in the plasma?
(a) hormones
(b) soluble food
(c) carbon dioxide
(d) oxygen   (1 mark)

5 Which of the following is not actually a blood cell?
(a) platelet
(b) lymphocyte
(c) red blood cell
(d) phagocyte   (1 mark)

Score   /5

B

Answer all parts of the questions.

1 The diagram shows a sample of blood.

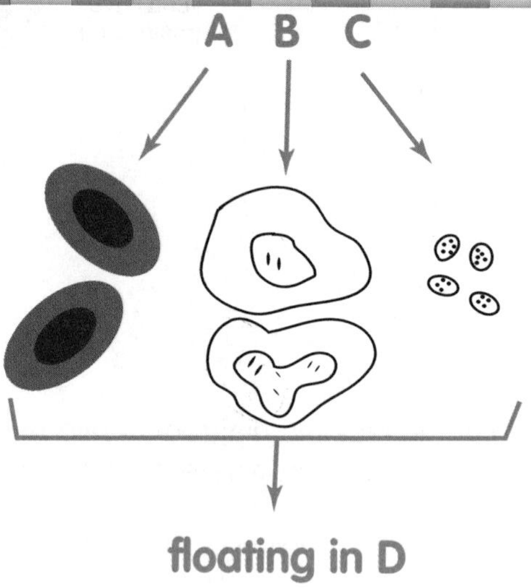

A B C

floating in D

(a) Name the cells A,B,C and the part labelled D.

A = ...

B = ...

C = ...

D = ...

(4 marks)

(b) Which of the parts

(i) carries carbon dioxide and glucose? ....

(ii) contains haemoglobin? ....

(iii) helps clot blood? ....

(iv) makes antibodies? ....

(4 marks)

Score   /8

C

These are GCSE-style questions. Answer all parts of the questions.

The diagram shows the major functions of blood.

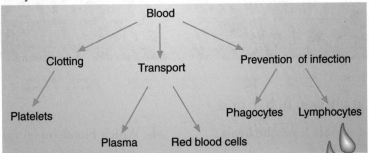

1 (a) Name two substances carried by the plasma.

.... (2 marks)

(b) (i) How is oxygen carried by the red blood cells and what substance is formed?

.... (2 marks)

(ii) How else are red blood cells adapted to carry oxygen?

.... (2 marks)

(c) How does blood clotting protect against disease?

.... (1 mark)

(d) What are the roles of

(i) phagocytes ....

(ii) lymphocytes .... (2 marks)

2 The table shows the number of red blood cells present in the blood of people living at different altitudes above sea level.

(a) As altitude increases, the amount of oxygen in the air decreases. Outline the relationship between the number of red blood cells and the height above sea level at which people live.

....

.... (1 mark)

(b) Explain the advantage of this change in number of red blood cells to people living at high altitude.

Height above sea level	Number of red blood cells
metres	million/mm^3 blood
0	5
1 000	5.6
2 000	6.2
3 000	6.6
4 000	7.4
5 000	7.8
6 000	8.1

.... (1 mark)

.... (2 marks)

Score   /13

How well did you do?

0–6 correct Try again
7–13 correct Getting there
14–20 correct Good work
21–26 correct Excellent!

TOTAL SCORE   /26

For more on this topic
see pages 12–13 of your Success Guide

HEART OF THE MATTER

A

Choose just one answer, a, b, c or d.

1 How many blood vessels leave the heart?
(a) 4   (c) 3
(b) 2   (d) 1   (1 mark)

2 Which part of the heart has the thickest walls?
(a) left ventricle
(b) left atrium
(c) right ventricle
(d) right atrium   (1 mark)

3 Which blood vessel contains valves?
(a) arterioles
(b) arteries
(c) veins
(d) capillaries   (1 mark)

4 Which blood vessel carries oxygenated blood?
(a) pulmonary artery
(b) vena cava
(c) jugular vein
(d) pulmonary vein   (1 mark)

5 Which blood vessels deliver oxygen and nutrients to the heart itself?
(a) coronary arteries
(b) pulmonary veins
(c) pulmonary artery
(d) vena cava   (1 mark)

Score   /5

B

Answer all parts of the questions.

In the table is a list of statements involved with three blood vessels. Tick the correct box if the statement relates to that particular blood vessel.

Statement	Arteries	Veins	Capillaries
carries blood at high pressure			
carries blood at low pressure			
has valves			
carries blood away from organs			
carries blood rich in carbon dioxide to the heart			
has walls that are one cell thick			
allows substances to pass through walls			
usually carries oxygenated blood			
supplies the heart with oxygen and nutrients			
are in close contact with body cells			
has thick elastic walls			

(11 marks)
Score   /11

C These are GCSE-style questions. Answer all parts of the questions.

The heart has its own supply of blood vessels called coronary arteries. Sometimes, a coronary artery gets blocked with fatty deposits; this can lead to a heart attack.

1 (a) What type of tissue is the heart made up of?

....

.... (1 mark)

(b) What is the function of this tissue?

.... (1 mark)

(c) The coronary arteries carry oxygen and glucose to the heart. Why does the heart tissue need these?

.... (1 mark)

(d) What will happen to the blood supply if the coronary arteries get blocked and what will the effect be on the heart?

....

....

.... (3 marks)

(e) Suggest some advice to the person in the diagram above to help them prevent the risk of developing a heart attack.

....

....

.... (3 marks)

2 (a) Label the diagram below of the heart.

A = ...

B = ...

C = ...

(3 marks)

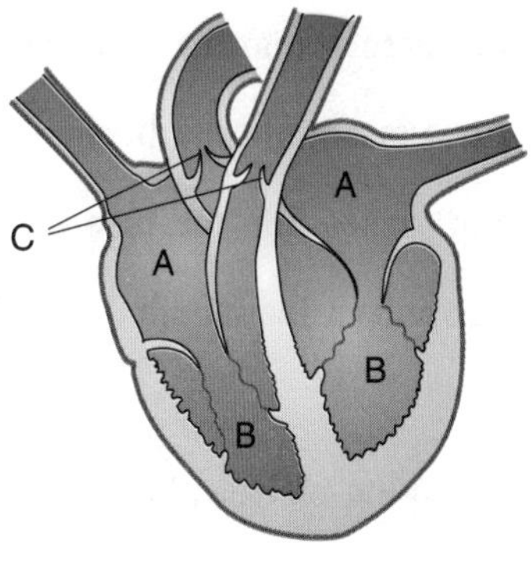

(b) Why does the heart contain valves?

.... (1 mark)

Score   /13

How well did you do?

0–7 correct Try again
8–14 correct Getting there
15–22 correct Good work
23–29 correct Excellent!

TOTAL SCORE   /29

For more on this topic
see pages 14–15 of your Success Guide

THE BREATHING SYSTEM

A

Choose just one answer, a, b, c or d.

1 Which of the following statements is true about breathing in?
(a) The ribs move down and in, the thorax volume decreases.
(b) The ribs move up and out, the thorax volume increases.
(c) the ribs move down and out, the thorax volume decreases.
(d) the ribs move up and in, the thorax volume increases. (1 mark)

2 What is the movement of air into and out of the lungs called?
(a) breathing
(b) respiration
(c) ventilation
(d) gas exchange (1 mark)

3 Which of these factors are important for gas exchange?
(a) thin walled alveoli
(b) thick walled alveoli
(c) large alveoli
(d) small alveoli (1 mark)

4 The trachea branches into?
(a) ribs   (c) bronchioles
(b) bronchi   (d) alveoli (1 mark)

5 Which gases are exchanged at the alveoli?
(a) oxygen and nitrogen
(b) oxygen and carbon dioxide
(c) carbon dioxide and nitrogen
(d) nitrogen and sulphur dioxide (1 mark)

Score   /5

B

Answer all parts of the questions.

1 Put these statements in the correct order for air travelling from the atmosphere to the blood.

(a) Air passes into the alveoli. ....

(b) Air passes down the trachea. ....

(c) Air passes into the bronchi. ....

(d) Air passes into the bronchioles. ....

(e) Air passes into the blood. ....

(f) Air enters the mouth. ....

(6 marks)

2 The following statements concern breathing. Are they true or false?

	True	False
(a) Inhaled air contains 0.03% carbon dioxide.	☐	☐
(b) Exhaled air contains approximately 16% oxygen.	☐	☐
(c) When we breathe in, the diaphragm relaxes.	☐	☐
(d) When we breathe out, the pressure inside our lungs decreases.	☐	☐
(e) The air we breathe out, is warmer than the air we breathe in.	☐	☐

(5 marks)

Score   /11

C **These are GCSE-style questions. Answer all parts of the questions.**

The diagram shows the breathing system in humans.

Trachea (wind pipe)

Bronchus

Intercostal muscle

Heart

Bronchiole

Rib

Pleural fluid

Alveoli

Diaphragm muscle

1 **(a)** State three ways in which the lungs are adapted for gas exchange.

....

....

.... (3 marks)

(b) Explain how the process of inhalation takes place. Use words from the diagram to help you.

....

....

.... (6 marks)

(c) Which gases are exchanged at the alveoli?

....

.... (2 marks)

(d) The air breathed into body often contains dust and bacteria. How are these prevented from entering the alveoli?

....

....

.... (3 marks)

(e) The air breathed out is cleaner than the air breathed in. Name two other differences.

....

.... (2 marks)

Score   /16

TOTAL SCORE   /32

For more on this topic
see pages 16–17 of your Success Guide

RESPIRATION

A Choose just one answer, a, b, c or d.

1 What are the products of respiration?
(a) carbon dioxide, water and energy
(b) oxygen and carbon dioxide
(c) oxygen and glucose
(d) water and energy   (1 mark)

2 Which gas is needed for respiration?
(a) sulphur dioxide
(b) oxygen
(c) carbon dioxide
(d) nitrogen   (1 mark)

3 How many oxygen molecules are made in respiration?
(a) 2   (c) 6
(b) 4   (d) 1   (1 mark)

4 What substance is made during anaerobic respiration in yeast?
(a) alcohol
(b) glucose
(c) lactic acid
(d) oxygen   (1 mark)

5 When do plants carry out respiration?
(a) in the day
(b) at night
(c) they only photosynthesise
(d) all the time   (1 mark)

Score   /5

B Answer all parts of the questions.

1 Read the following information

Respiration takes place in the mitochondria of cells. Chemical reactions take place that use up oxygen and glucose and produce carbon dioxide and water. The process also releases energy.

Use the above information to complete the diagram below.

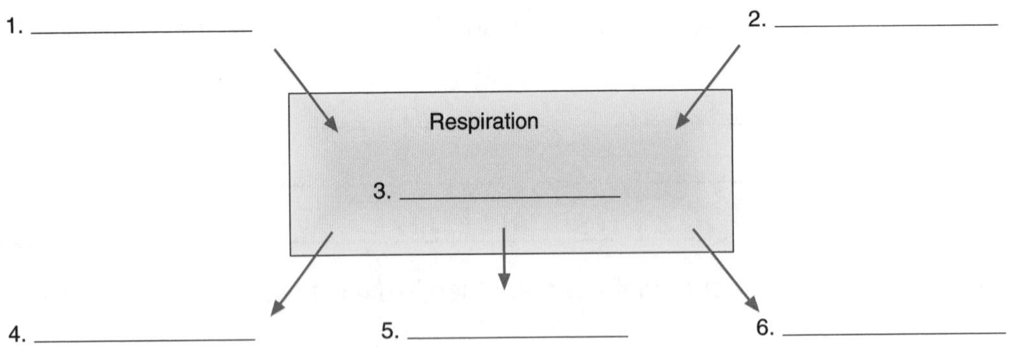

1. _____

2. _____

Respiration

3. _____

4. _____   5. _____   6. _____

(6 marks)

2 Name four uses of the energy produced in respiration.

....

....

....

....

(4 marks)

Score   /10

C **These are GCSE-style questions. Answer all parts of the questions.**

The graph shows the level of lactic acid in the blood before, during and after exercise.

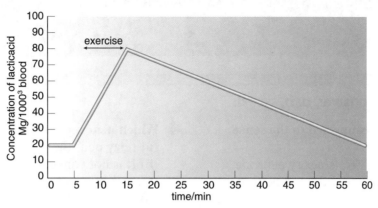

1 **(a)** What is the normal level of lactic acid in the blood?

.... (1 mark)

(b) By how much did it increase during exercise?

.... (1 mark)

(c) How long after exercise did it take to return to normal?

.... (1 mark)

(d) Name the process that produces lactic acid in the blood.

.... (1 mark)

(e) When does the process in **(d)** occur?

.... (1 mark)

(f) After exercise the amount of oxygen breathed in needs to increase. Explain why.

....

.... (2 marks)

2 Anaerobic respiration in yeast is shown by the equation

glucose → alcohol + carbon dioxide + energy

(a) Write down the equation for anaerobic respiration in humans.

.... (1 mark)

(b) State a difference between the two reactions.

....

.... (2 marks)

Score   /10

TOTAL SCORE   /25

For more on this topic
see pages 18–19 of your Success Guide

THE NERVOUS SYSTEM

A Choose just one answer, a, b, c or d.

1 Which neurone is connected to the sense organ?
(a) relay neurone   (c) sensory neurone
(b) motor neurone   (d) all three neurones
(1 mark)

2 What is a synapse?
(a) a gap between neurones
(b) part of the sense organ
(c) part of the spinal cord
(d) part of the brain   (1 mark)

3 What diffuses across a synapse?
(a) oxygen
(b) a chemical
(c) a relay neurone
(d) a hormone   (1 mark)

4 Which neurone is connected to the effector?
(a) relay neurone
(b) It is not connected to anything.
(c) sensory neurone
(d) motor neurone   (1 mark)

5 Which organs detect changes in the environment?
(a) sense organs
(b) the liver
(c) the heart
(d) the lungs   (1 mark)

Score   /5

B Answer all parts of the questions.

1 True or false?

	True	False
(a) Reflex actions are controlled by the brain.	☐	☐
(b) Hormonal responses are faster than nervous responses.	☐	☐
(c) A synapse is a gap between neurones.	☐	☐
(d) Our sense organs contain receptors.	☐	☐
(e) The CNS stands for Central Nerve Syndrome.	☐	☐

(5 marks)

2 Match up the word with its definition.

Relay neurone — receives messages from the sense organs

Sensory neurone — sends messages to a muscle or a gland

Motor neurone — connects two neurones together

(3 marks)

Score   /8

C **These are GCSE-style questions. Answer all parts of the questions.**

1 The diagram below shows a reflex arc pathway.

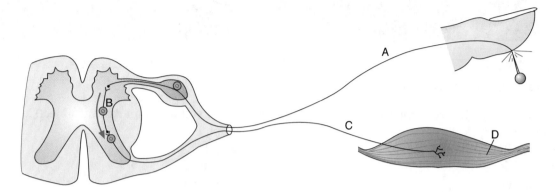

(a) Name the parts labelled

   (i) A ....

   (ii) B ....

   (iii)C ....

   (iv)D .... (4 marks)

(b) Draw arrows on the diagram to show the direction of the nervous impulse from

   (i) B to C

   (ii) C to D (2 marks)

(c) What is the name of the gap between parts A and B and B and C?

.... (1 mark)

(d) How does the nervous impulse cross the gap named in C?

.... (1 mark)

2 Name the response that would be produced by each of the following stimuli.

(a) (i) dust in the eye ....

   (ii) dust in the mouth ....

   (iii)a bright light ....

   (iv)the smell of food .... (4 marks)

(b) What is the name given to these types of responses?

.... (1 mark)

Score   /13

How well did you do?

0–6 correct: Try again

7–13 correct: Getting there

14–20 correct: Good work

21–26 correct: Excellent!

TOTAL SCORE   /26

For more on this topic
see pages 20–21 of your Success Guide

THE EYE

A

Choose just one answer, a, b, c or d.

1 Which part of the eye changes in response to light?
(a) the ciliary muscles
(b) the iris
(c) the retina
(d) the sclera (1 mark)

2 Which part of the eye changes shape to focus?
(a) the lens (c) the cornea
(b) the retina (d) the pupil (1 mark)

3 What happens to the ciliary muscles when you focus on close objects?
(a) They curve.
(b) They relax.
(c) They contract.
(d) They stay the same. (1 mark)

4 When you focus on distant objects, what shape is the lens?
(a) fat
(b) round
(c) stays the same
(d) thin (1 mark)

5 Which part of the eye sends messages to the brain?
(a) the optic nerve
(b) the sclerotic layer
(c) the cornea
(d) the iris (1 mark)

Score /5

B

Answer all parts of the questions.

1 Label this diagram of the eye.

A = ...

B = ...

C = ...

D = ...

(clear window in front of C)

(4 marks)

2 Match the following parts of the eye to its function.

| retina | iris | lens | cornea | sclera | pupil |

(a) contains light sensitive cells ....

(b) controls the amount of light entering the eye ....

(c) alters its shape to focus on objects ....

(d) gets smaller in bright light ....

(e) touch outer layer ....

(f) transparent layer ....

(6 marks)

Score /10

C These are GCSE-style questions. Answer all parts of the questions.

1 The diagram below is a section of the eye.

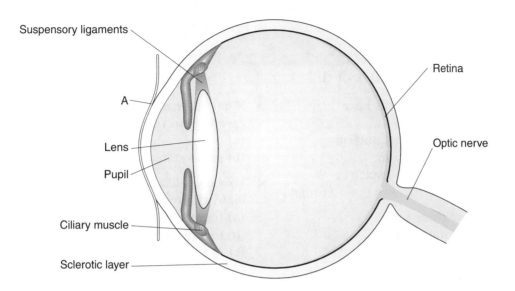

Suspensory ligaments

Retina

A

Lens

Optic nerve

Pupil

Ciliary muscle

Sclerotic layer

(a) Name the part labelled A and describe its appearance.

....

.... (2 marks)

(b) Using the labels above, describe how a near object is focused on the retina.

....

....

....

....

....

.... (5 marks)

2 (a) What is the function of the iris?

.... (1 mark)

(b) Under what conditions is the pupil

(i) smaller ....

(ii) larger .... (2 marks)

Score   /10

How well did you do?
0–5 correct Try again
6–12 correct Getting there
13–19 correct Good work
20–25 correct Excellent!

TOTAL SCORE   /25

For more on this topic
see pages 22–23 of your Success Guide

CELLS

A **Choose just one answer, a, b, c or d.**

1 What do animal and plant cells have in common?
(a) cell membrane, cytoplasm, nucleus
(b) vacuole, nucleus, cytoplasm
(c) cell membrane, cell wall, nucleus
(d) cell wall, nucleus, cytoplasm (1 mark)

2 What is a cell membrane for?
(a) It is there to contain cell sap.
(b) controlling what passes in and out of the cell
(c) It is where chemical reactions take place.
(d) controlling the activities of the cell (1 mark)

3 What is the name given to a group of cells carrying out the same job?
(a) organ (c) specialised cells
(b) organ system (d) tissue (1 mark)

4 Why do palisade cells contain so many chloroplasts?
(a) for extra support
(b) to absorb sunlight for photosynthesis
(c) to keep the leaf in shape
(d) to help them absorb water (1 mark)

5 Which cell is the odd one out?
(a) palisade cell (c) nerve cell
(b) sperm cell (d) muscle cell (1 mark)

Score /5

B **Answer all parts of the questions.**

1 Below is a list of specialised cells. Underline the animal cells.

sperm cell

red blood cell

root hair cell

nerve cell

palisade cell

guard cell

(3 marks)

2 True or false?

	True	False
(a) All living things are made up of cells.	☐	☐
(b) Both animal and plant cells are made up of cell walls.	☐	☐
(c) All human cells have a nucleus.	☐	☐
(d) An organ is a group of cells with the same structure and function.	☐	☐
(e) All animal cells contain cytoplasm.	☐	☐
(f) Vacuoles are found in most animal cells.	☐	☐
(g) Animal and plant cells contain mitochondria.	☐	☐

(7 marks)

Score /10

C

These are GCSE-style questions. Answer all parts of the questions.

1 The diagrams show several types of specialised cells.

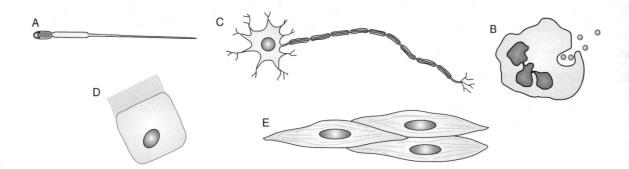

(a) Name each type of cell.

A .... D ....

B .... E ....

C .... (5 marks)

(b) Give the letter of the cell that

(i) has half the normal number of chromosomes ....

(ii) traps dust and bacteria ....

(iii) carries information as electrical impulses ....

(iv) lines the respiratory system ....

(v) can ingest bacteria .... (6 marks)

(c) What is the function of cell E?

.... (1 mark)

2 (a) There are three main differences between a typical plant cell and a typical animal cell. What are they?

....

....

.... (3 marks)

(b) The cells in question **1** are all specialised animal cells. Name three specialised plant cells.

....

....

.... (3 marks)

Score   /18

How well did you do?

0–8 correct Try again
9–17 correct Getting there
18–26 correct Good work
27–33 correct Excellent!

TOTAL SCORE   /33

For more on this topic see pages 26–27 of your Success Guide

DIFFUSION, OSMOSIS AND ACTIVE TRANSPORT

A Choose just one answer, a, b, c or d.

1 Which of these is not an example of diffusion?
(a) the smell of perfume from a person passing by
(b) the smell of a lit match in the room
(c) oxygen being breathed out
(d) oxygen passing into the blood   (1 mark)

2 Which of the following methods of transport is the odd one out?
(a) diffusion of liquids (c) diffusion of gases
(b) active transport   (d) osmosis   (1 mark)

3 Partially permeable membrane means
(a) It has tiny holes in it.
(b) It lets anything through.
(c) It has large holes in it.
(d) It does not let any substance through.
(1 mark)

4 Which term describes a cell that is full of water?
(a) flaccid   (c) haemolysed
(b) plasmolysed   (d) turgid   (1 mark)

5 What happens to animal cells that are placed in water?
(a) They plasmolyse
(b) They become flaccid
(c) They burst
(d) They become turgid   (1 mark)

Score   /5

B Answer all parts of the questions.

1 Look at the following diagram.

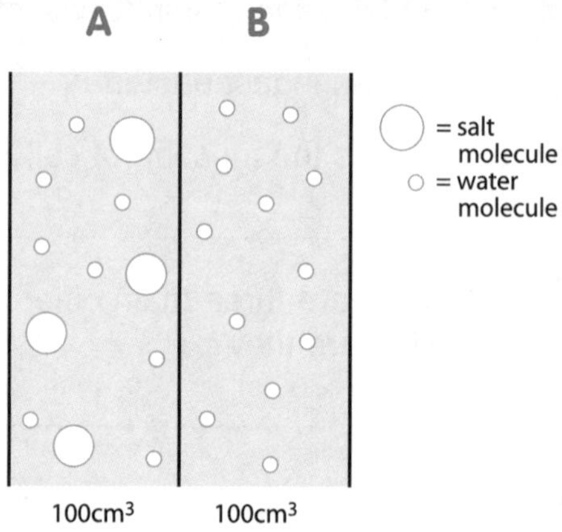

(a) Draw an arrow showing the direction the water molecules will move.

(1 mark)

(b) What is the movement of water molecules called?

....

....   (1 mark)

A   B

○ = salt molecule
○ = water molecule

100cm³   100cm³

2 Put a tick if the statement is correct for the three methods of movement of molecules.

	Diffusion	Osmosis	Active transport
Molecules move from high to low concentration.			
Movement requires energy.			
Molecules travel against the concentration gradient.			
Movement takes place in animal and plant cells.			

(7 marks)

Score   /9

C These are GCSE-style questions. Answer all parts of the questions.

1 Seven cylinders of potato, each of the same mass, were placed into different concentrations of salt solution. After 3 hours they were removed and their mass was measured. The table below shows the results.

Concentration of salt (%)							
	0	2	4	6	8	10	12
Start mass (g)	5	5	5	5	5	5	5
After 3 hours (g)	5.5	5.3	5	4.8	4.6	4.4	4.2

(a) Plot a graph to the right of the results after 3 hours.

(3 marks)

(b) (i) In which concentration of salts did the potato gain in mass?

....

.... (1 mark)

(ii) Explain how the gain in mass was caused.

....

....

.... (4 marks)

(c) (i) Calculate the percentage decrease in mass in the potato cylinder in 6% salt solution.

....

.... (2 marks)

(ii) Explain why the potato lost mass.

....

.... (3 marks)

(d) (i) Which concentration of salt solution had no effect on the potato mass?

.... (1 mark)

(ii) Explain why the potato did not gain or lose mass.

....

.... (3 marks)

Score /17

How well did you do?

0–8 correct Try again
9–17 correct Getting there
18–25 correct Good work
26–31 correct Excellent!

TOTAL SCORE /31

For more on this topic
see pages 28–29 of your Success Guide

PLANT AND LEAF

Choose just one answer, a, b, c or d.

1 Which of the following cells opens and closes the stomata?
(a) epidermis cells   (c) guard cells
(b) palisade cells   (d) spongy layer cells
(1 mark)

2 Which of the following cells carries water and minerals?
(a) xylem cells   (c) phloem cells
(b) guard cells   (d) palisade cells   (1 mark)

3 Which layer in the leaf allows carbon dioxide into the leaf?
(a) the upper surface
(b) the bottom layer
(c) the middle layer
(d) the top layer   (1 mark)

4 Which part of the plant holds it upright?
(a) the root hairs
(b) the stem
(c) the leaf
(d) the root   (1 mark)

5 Where is water absorbed into a plant?
(a) the flower
(b) the leaf
(c) the root
(d) the root hairs   (1 mark)

Score   /5

B

Answer all parts of the questions.

1 Match the plant parts below with the following characteristics.

root   stem   root hairs   flower   leaf

(a) absorbs water from the soil   ....
(b) produces glucose   ....
(c) produces pollen   ....
(d) anchors a plant in the soil   ....
(e) contains xylem and phloem   ....
(5 marks)

flower, leaf, stem, root hairs, root

2 Match the part of the leaf with its function by drawing single lines.

controls the opening and closing of stomata   spongy layer

allows gases to circulate   palisade layer

contains xylem and phloem   guard cells

contains many chloroplasts   stomata

allows carbon dioxide in   leaf vein

(5 marks)

Score   /10

C These are GCSE-style questions. Answer all parts of the questions.

1 The diagram shows a section through a leaf.

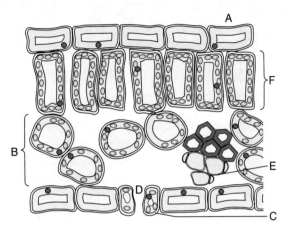

(a) Which of the structures labelled on the diagram

  (i) is where most photosynthesis takes place ....

  (ii) forms a waterproof layer ....

  (iii) allows gases in and out ....

  (iv) controls the amount of water vapour leaving the leaf ....

  (v) allows gases to circulate ....

  (vi) contains xylem and phloem ....   (6 marks)

(b) Name the parts of the leaf represented by the letters

A ....   D ....

B ....   E ....

C ....   F ....   (6 marks)

(c) The leaf's function is to carry out photosynthesis and make food for the plant, what are the functions of the

  (i) roots ....

  (ii) root hairs ....

  (iii) stem ....   (3 marks)

2 Describe how water is carried from the soil to the leaf.

....

....

....   (3 marks)

Score   /18

How well did you do?

0–8 correct   Try again
9–17 correct   Getting there
18–26 correct   Good work
27–33 correct   Excellent!

TOTAL SCORE   /33

For more on this topic
see pages 30–31 of your Success Guide

PLANT SENSES

A

Choose just one answer, a, b, c or d.

1 What is a plants response to gravity called?
(a) hydrotropism
(b) geotropism
(c) phototropism
(d) autotropism (1 mark)

2 What is the name of the hormone that controls plant growth?
(a) auxin   (c) troxin
(b) nitroxin   (d) oestrogen (1 mark)

3 Which of these is not a use of synthetic hormones?
(a) producing seedless fruits
(b) killing weeds
(c) making plants look nicer
(d) making fruits ripen early (1 mark)

4 What effect does auxin have on the growth of shoots?
(a) It slows down growth.
(b) It has no effect.
(c) It prevents growth.
(d) It speeds up growth. (1 mark)

5 A plant does not respond to
(a) water   (c) food
(b) light   (d) gravity (1 mark)

Score /5

B

Answer all parts of the question.

1 (a) Plants' responses to stimuli are called tropisms.

What is a plant's response to the following stimuli called?

(i) water ....tropism

(ii) gravity ....tropism

(iii) light ....tropism (3 marks)

(b) Add another plant to the one below to show what happens to the plant when a light is shone from the left-hand side.

1   2 (1 mark)

(c) Shade on your diagram where the hormone collects that causes this movement. (1 mark)

Score /5

C

These are GCSE-style questions. Answer all parts of the questions.

1 A seed was planted into the ground upside-down. A root began to grow down into the soil and a shoot upwards towards the light.

(a) What caused the root and the shoot to grow in the directions they did?

....

.... (2 marks)

(b) On the diagram below shade where the hormone would have collected on the root and the shoot.

shoot

seed

root

(2 marks)

(c) What effect does the hormone have on the rate of growth of a

(i) root ....

(ii) shoot ....

(2 marks)

(d) how do plants respond to

(i) light ....

(ii) water ....

(iii) gravity ....

(3 marks)

2 Synthetic hormones are often used for commercial purposes. State three ways they can be used.

....

....

.... (3 marks)

Score   /12

How well did you do?

0–5 correct Try again
6–11 correct Getting there
12–17 correct Good work
18–22 correct Excellent!

TOTAL SCORE   /22

For more on this topic
see pages 32–33 of your Success Guide

PLANT TRANSPORT AND GOOD HEALTH

A

Choose just one answer, a, b, c or d.

1 **What is transpiration?**
(a) the loss of water
(b) the gain of water
(c) the flow of sugar through the plant
(d) the gain of carbon dioxide   (1 mark)

2 **What are the effects of a lack of nitrate on a plant?**
(a) purple leaves with dead spots
(b) poor root growth and purple leaves
(c) yellow leaves with dead spots
(d) stunted growth and yellow leaves   (1 mark)

3 **What are the effects of a lack of potassium on a plant?**
(a) stunted growth and purple leaves
(b) yellow leaves with dead spots
(c) poor root growth and purple leaves
(d) yellow leaves and stunted growth   (1 mark)

4 **What are the effects of a lack of phosphates on a plant?**
(a) stunted growth and poor root growth
(b) purple leaves and dead spots
(c) poor root growth and purple leaves
(d) no effect   (1 mark)

5 **Which vessels are responsible for transporting food around a plant?**
(a) xylem vessels
(b) cambian vessels
(c) vascular bundle vessels
(d) phloem vessels   (1 mark)

Score   /5

B

Answer all parts of the questions.

1 Complete the following sentences.

(a) Transpiration is the .... of water out of a plant's stomata by ....

(b) The rate of transpiration is affected by the amount of .... , ... , ... and humidity.

(c) Transpiration is fastest in .... , ... and .... conditions.
(8 marks)

2 Cross out the incorrect words in the following passage.

Plant cells that lose water become flaccid/turgid. Plant cells that obtain enough water are said to be flaccid/turgid. Plants transport the food they make in their leaves in tubes called phloem/xylem vessels and they transport water in tubes called phloem/xylem vessels.

(4 marks)

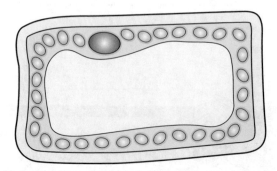

Score   /12

C These are GCSE-style questions. Answer all parts of the questions.

1 A student was investigating the effects of mineral ions on the growth of plants. Four identical tubes were set up.

1. Tube contained all minerals

2. Tube contained all minerals except nitrate

3. Tube contained all minerals except potassium

4. Tube contained all minerals except phosphate

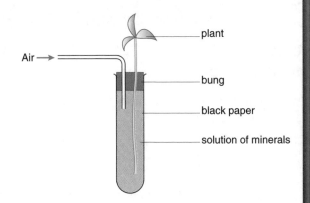

The diagram shows the apparatus used.

(a) Why was air bubbled through the solution?

.... (1 mark)

(b) Suggest a reason why black paper covered the test tube.

....

.... (2 marks)

(c) How could the growth of the plant be measured?

.... (1 mark)

(d) After 1 month the plants were examined, the plant in tube 1 showed normal healthy growth but the other plants showed signs of mineral deficiencies. Describe the appearance of the plants in

(i) tube 2 ....

....

....

(ii) tube 3 ....

....

....

(iii) tube 4 ....

....

.... (6 marks)

Score   /10

How well did you do?

0–6 correct Try again
7–14 correct Getting there
15–21 correct Good work
22–27 correct Excellent!

TOTAL SCORE   /27

For more on this topic
see pages 34–35 of your Success Guide

PHOTOSYNTHESIS

A Choose just one answer, a, b, c or d.

1 When does photosynthesis take place?
(a) in the winter
(b) at night
(c) in the day
(d) night and day   (1 mark)

2 Which of these factors is not a limiting factor in photosynthesis?
(a) oxygen
(b) light
(c) temperature
(d) carbon dioxide   (1 mark)

3 Which type of cells contains many chloroplasts?
(a) xylem   (c) stomata
(b) palisade cells (d) phloem   (1 mark)

4 What substance does a plant store glucose as?
(a) sugar
(b) proteins
(c) starch
(d) maltose   (1 mark)

5 What are the products of photosynthesis?
(a) glucose and oxygen
(b) carbon dioxide and water
(c) oxygen and carbon dioxide
(d) water and oxygen   (1 mark)

Score   /5

B Answer all parts of the question.

1 The diagram shows some of the ways in which plants use the carbohydrate they produce.

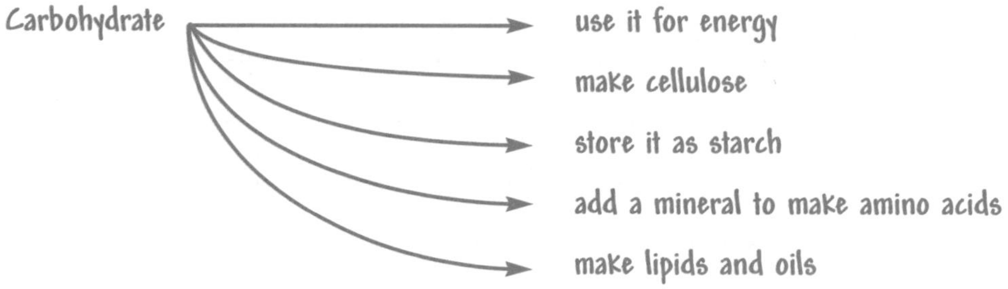

Carbohydrate →
use it for energy
make cellulose
store it as starch
add a mineral to make amino acids
make lipids and oils

(a) What is cellulose used for? .... (1 mark)

(b) What mineral is needed to make amino acids? .... (1 mark)

(c) How does a plant obtain its minerals? ....
.... (2 marks)

(d) Why do plants store carbohydrate as starch ....
....
.... (3 marks)

(e) In what form is the carbohydrate used for energy? .... (1 mark)

(f) What process uses carbohydrates to make energy? .... (1 mark)

Score   /9

36

C   These are GCSE-style questions. Answer all parts of the question.

1 The graph shows the effect of carbon dioxide concentration on the rate of photosynthesis of a plant in a greenhouse.

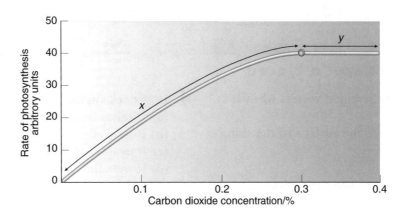

(a) Suggest a factor that is limiting the rate of photosynthesis at X.

.... (1 mark)

(b) Suggest a factor that is limiting the rate of photosynthesis at Y.

.... (1 mark)

(c) Describe the relationship between level of carbon dioxide and the rate of photosynthesis.

....

.... (2 marks)

(d) In winter commercial plant growers often use greenhouses to grow their plants. They sometimes burn fossil fuels in the greenhouses. Suggest how this helps increase the growth rate of plants.

....

.... (2 marks)

(e) What other factors must the growers consider when growing plants in a greenhouse?

....

.... (2 marks)

(f) Sometimes heaters are used in greenhouses. Why are they not necessary in the summer?

....

....

.... (3 marks)

Score   /11

How well did you do?

0–5 correct Try again
6–12 correct Getting there
13–18 correct Good work
19–25 correct Excellent!

TOTAL SCORE   /25

For more on this topic
see pages 36–37 of your Success Guide

THE SKIN

A Choose just one answer, a, b, c or d.

1 What happens to the blood vessels when it is hot?
(a) They move up to the surface of the skin.
(b) They widen.
(c) They contract.
(d) They move away from the surface of the skin. **(1 mark)**

2 What happens to body hair when it is cold?
(a) It lays flat.
(b) It starts to fall out.
(c) It stands up.
(d) It grows faster. **(1 mark)**

3 What radiates from the skin?
(a) heat   (c) water
(b) sweat   (d) cool air   **(1 mark)**

4 How does sweating cool the body down?
(a) It takes hot water away from the body.
(b) It helps the body to keep water.
(c) It evaporates taking away heat energy.
(d) It wets the skin cooling it down.   **(1 mark)**

5 What is the normal body temperature?
(a) 37 °C
(b) 40 °C
(c) 39 °C
(d) 44 °C   **(1 mark)**

Score   /5

B Answer all parts of the questions.

1 Cross out the incorrect words in the following passage.

When it is hot, blood vessels at the surface constrict/dilate so more/less blood gets to the surface of the skin. The sweat glands stop/start producing sweat. Hairs on the body lie flat/stand up. More heat is lost by radiation/conduction.

(5 marks)

2 True or false?

	True	False
(a) Normal body temperature for humans is 39 degrees Celsius.	☐	☐
(b) When blood vessels widen, it is called vasodilation.	☐	☐
(c) Sweating cools the body down.	☐	☐
(d) Vasoconstriction is when the blood vessels dilate.	☐	☐
(e) In cold weather less blood reaches the surface of the skin.	☐	☐

Section of human skin

(5 marks)

Score   /10

C **These are GCSE-style questions. Answer all parts of the questions.**

1 The diagram shows the blood vessels in the skin.

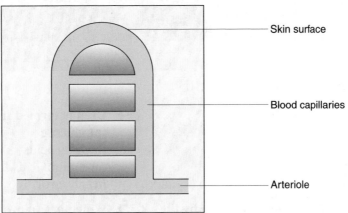

Skin surface

Blood capillaries

Arteriole

(a) When the body temperature falls, what happens to the arterioles and what is the process called?

....

.... (2 marks)

(b) What are the effects of this change in the arterioles?

....

....

.... (3 marks)

(c) Explain why humans shiver in cold conditions.

....

.... (2 marks)

(d) How does sweating help maintain the human body temperature at normal?

....

....

....

.... (4 marks)

(e) What other mechanisms does the human body use to maintain body temperature when the temperature rises? Explain how they help lower the body temperature to normal.

....

....

....

.... (4 marks)

Score   /15

How well did you do?

0–7 correct Try again
8–14 correct Getting there
15–23 correct Good work
24–30 correct Excellent!

TOTAL SCORE   /30

**For more on this topic
see pages 38–39 of your Success Guide**

THE KIDNEYS 1

A

Choose just one answer, a, b, c or d.

1 What is the function of the kidneys?
(a) excretion
(b) movement
(c) respiration
(d) reproduction (1 mark)

2 Which waste product is only removed by the kidneys?
(a) water
(b) urea
(c) carbon dioxide
(d) glucose (1 mark)

3 Which hormone is involved in water regulation?
(a) FSH   (c) LH
(b) TSH   (d) ADH (1 mark)

4 Urea is formed from which substance?
(a) glucose
(b) fatty acids
(c) amino acids
(d) glycerol (1 mark)

5 Which organ produces urea?
(a) the stomach
(b) the large intestine
(c) the kidneys
(d) the liver (1 mark)

Score /5

B

Answer all parts of the questions.

| lungs | skin | kidneys |

1 Which of the above organs do the following?

(a) remove water ....

(b) remove salt and water ....

(c) remove carbon dioxide ....

(d) remove urea in large amounts ....

(e) help maintain body temperature .... (5 marks)

2 Fully label the diagram of the kidneys.

A = ...
B = ...
C = ...
D = ...
E = ...
F = ...
G = ...
H = ...

(8 marks)

Score /13

C These are GCSE-style questions. Answer all parts of the questions.

1 People who suffer from kidney failure may be treated by dialysis. The diagram shows a simple dialysis machine.

Dialysis fluid in

Dialysis fluid out   Blood out

Blood in

(a) For each substance, state whether the blood leaving the dialysis machine to go back into the patient contains more, less, or the same amount, of

  (i) glucose ....

  (ii) salt ....

  (iii) water ....

  (iv) urea ....   (4 marks)

(b) The blood entering the dialysis machine forces out glucose into the surrounding fluid that makes up the patient's urine. Explain why glucose is not found in the urine at the end of dialysis?

....
                                                                                                (1 mark)

2 The graph below shows the level of ADH in the blood and the rate at which urine is formed.

Urine formation cm³/min

ADH

Urine

Time/min

(a) What is the normal rate of urine production?

.... (1 mark)

(b) What effect does the fall in level of ADH have on the rate of urine production?

.... (1 mark)

(c) Describe how ADH controls the amount of water in the blood when a person has not consumed a lot of fluids.

....

....

....

....
                                                                                                (5 marks)

Score   /12

How well did you do?

0–7 correct Try again
8–15 correct Getting there
16–23 correct Good work
24–30 correct Excellent!

TOTAL SCORE   /30

For more on this topic
see pages 40–41 of your Success Guide

THE KIDNEYS 2

A **Choose just one answer, a, b, c or d.**

1 Which substance is completely re-absorbed by the kidneys?
(a) water   (c) urea
(b) glucose   (d) salt   (1 mark)

2 Name the artery that enters the kidneys.
(a) pulmonary artery
(b) aorta
(c) renal artery
(d) hepatic artery   (1 mark)

3 What happens to urine under the influence of the homone ADH?
(a) it becomes concentrated
(b) it becomes dilute
(c) it increases in volume
(d) it decreases in volume   (1 mark)

4 What is the name of the group of blood capillaries in the kidney?
(a) collecting ducts
(b) glomerulus
(c) nephron
(d) bowmans capsule   (1 mark)

5 What is the name of the tube leading to the bladder from the kidneys?
(a) urethra
(b) aorta
(c) ureter
(d) renal tube   (1 mark)

Score /5

B **Answer all parts of the questions.**

1 True or false?

	True	False
(a) Urine is produced by the bladder.	☐	☐
(b) The kidney breaks down amino acids and produces urea.	☐	☐
(c) The presence of sugar in the urine is a sign of diabetes.	☐	☐
(d) In hot weather the concentration of urine increases.	☐	☐
(e) Homeostasis involves keeping the internal environment constant.	☐	☐
(f) The glomerulus is a group of blood capillaries in the kidney.	☐	☐
(g) The renal artery contains filtered blood.	☐	☐
(h) Osmoregulation is the control of water in the blood.	☐	☐
(i) Urine flows out of the body in the urethra.	☐	☐

(9 marks)

2 Number these sentences to show in the order they happen during blood flow through the kidney nephron

(a) Filtered blood leaves the nephron in the renal vein. ....

(b) Blood arrives in the renal artery. ....

(c) High pressure forces molecules into the bowmans capsule. ....

(d) Useful molecules are re-absorbed and flow into the renal vein. ....

(e) Blood enters a group of capillaries called the glomerulus. .... (5 marks)

Score /14

C **These are GCSE-style questions. Answer all parts of the questions.**

The bar chart shows the amounts of various substances filtered and re-absorbed by the kidneys each day.

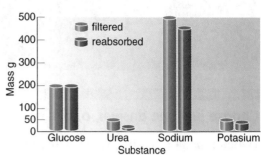

(a) From the graph, which substance is completely re-absorbed?

.... (1 mark)

(b) Why is the substance in **(a)** completely re-absorbed?

.... (1 mark)

(c) Which organ in the body forms urea and which substance is it formed from?

....

.... (2 marks)

(d) How much urea is excreted by the kidneys?

.... (1 mark)

(e) How much potassium is excreted by the kidneys?

.... (1 mark)

(f) The volume of water filtered by the kidneys is approximately 150 litres per day. Of this, 1.5 litres is excreted. What volume of water is re-absorbed?

....

.... (2 marks)

2 **(a)** Name the hormone, which controls the amount of water that is re-absorbed by the kidneys.

.... (1 mark)

(b) Which of the substances in the chart would be excreted in large amounts by a

(i) diabetic?

....

(ii) A person with a high protein diet?

....

.... (2 marks)

Score   /11

How well did you do?

0–7 correct   Try again
8–16 correct   Getting there
17–23 correct   Good work
24–30 correct   Excellent!

TOTAL SCORE   /30

For more on this topic see pages 40–41 of your Success Guide

CAUSES OF DISEASE

A

Choose just one answer, a, b, c or d.

1 Which type of microbe produces toxins?
  (**a**) bacteria   (**c**) all of them
  (**b**) virus   (**d**) fungi   (1 mark)

2 Which of the following is caused by a virus?
  (**a**) athlete's foot
  (**b**) HIV
  (**c**) whooping cough
  (**d**) tetanus   (1 mark)

3 Which of the following cells do not have a nucleus?
  (**a**) white blood cells
  (**b**) sperm cells
  (**c**) palisade cells
  (**d**) virus cells   (1 mark)

4 Which type of microbe is used for making beer and wine?
  (**a**) virus
  (**b**) bacteria
  (**c**) fungi
  (**d**) virus and fungi   (1 mark)

5 Which of the following diseases are caused by bacteria?
  (**a**) salmonella
  (**b**) chicken pox
  (**c**) measles
  (**d**) ringworm   (1 mark)

Score   /5

B

Answer all parts of the question.

1 (a) Complete the following table. Use words already in the table.

Name of disease	Microbe	Method of spread	Method of treatment
polio	virus	air and water	immunisation
measles		air	
chicken pox		air	immunisation
tetanus	bacteria	infected cuts	
tuberculosis	bacteria	air	immunisation
food poisoning		contaminated food	
pneumonia			antibiotics

(8 marks)

(b) What do the diseases treated by antibiotics have in common?

.... (1 mark)

Score   /9

C **These are GCSE-style questions. Answer all parts of the questions.**

1 (a) Microbes such as bacteria can cause diseases. Name two other types of microbe.

....

.... (2 marks)

(b) The diagram shows a bacterial cell.

Cell wall

Cell membrane

Genes   Cytoplasm

Use the information in the diagram to describe the appearance of the bacterial cell.

....

....

.... (3 marks)

(c) How does a bacterial cell compare to a virus?

....

.... (2 marks)

2 (a) Explain how microbes cause disease.

....

....

....

....

.... (5 marks)

(b) Name four ways in which microbes can enter the body.

....

....

....

.... (4 marks)

Score   /16

How well did you do?

0–8 correct Try again
9–16 correct Getting there
17–23 correct Good work
24–30 correct Excellent!

TOTAL SCORE   /30

For more on this topic
see pages 42–43 of your Success Guide

DEFENCE AGAINST DISEASE

A Choose just one answer, a, b, c or d.

1 Which part of the body forms a barrier against infection?
(a) the skin
(b) the respiratory system
(c) the stomach
(d) the digestive system (1 mark)

2 What are vaccines?
(a) antibiotics
(b) injections
(c) harmless/weak microbes
(d) antiseptics (1 mark)

3 What is the name of the drugs used to treat bacterial infections?
(a) antitoxins   (c) vaccines
(b) antiseptics   (d) antibiotics   (1 mark)

4 What cell is involved in the immune response?
(a) red blood cells
(b) ciliated cells
(c) white blood cells
(d) skin cells (1 mark)

5 What chemicals do white blood cells produce?
(a) antibodies
(b) antibiotics
(c) antiseptics
(d) antitoxins (1 mark)

Score   /5

B Answer all parts of the questions.

1 Write in the name of the correct organ that prevents the entry of microbes in the way described.

How the organ prevents entry	Name of organ
Produces clots to seal wounds	
Acts as a barrier	
Produces sticky mucus	
Produces acid	
Secretes an antiseptic called lysosome	

(5 marks)

2 True or false?

	True	False
(a) Viruses can be treated with antibiotics.	☐	☐
(b) Natural immunity is administered by injection.	☐	☐
(c) Antiseptics are drugs taken by mouth.	☐	☐
(d) Lymphocytes produce chemicals called antibodies.	☐	☐
(e) Vaccines contain dead or harmless germs.	☐	☐

(5 marks)

Score   /10

C **These are GCSE-style questions. Answer all parts of the questions.**

1 Bacteria were grown on a nutrient agar plate. An investigation was carried out to find which of five antibiotics was the most effective against these bacteria. Discs of filter paper soaked in the same amount of the five different antibiotics were placed on the plate.

Agar nutrient plate

(a) Which of the antibiotics was the

   (i) most effective ....

   (ii) least effective ....

(2 marks)

(b) What causes the clear area around the filter paper?

....

.... (2 marks)

(c) Why does a course of antibiotics have to be followed to the end?

.... (1 mark)

(d) Why would antibiotics not be prescribed to a person suffering from measles?

....

.... (2 marks)

2 (a) The body can fight microbes once they enter the body using its immune system. How does the immune system work in the first instance?

....

....

.... (3 marks)

(b) How does the body gain immunity to a disease?

....

....

.... (3 marks)

Score   /13

How well did you do?

0–7 correct Try again
8–14 correct Getting there
15–21 correct Good work
22–28 correct Excellent!

TOTAL SCORE   /28

For more on this topic
see pages 44–45 of your Success Guide

DRUGS, SOLVENTS, ALCOHOL AND TOBACCO

A **Choose just one answer, a, b, c or d.**

1 Which part of the body do drugs affect the most?
(a) blood vessels   (c) brain
(b) liver   (d) lungs   (1 mark)

2 Sedatives are drugs that
(a) slow reactions
(b) give you energy
(c) speed up reactions
(d) cause hallucinations   (1 mark)

3 Hallucinogens are drugs that
(a) are used to treat stress and anxiety
(b) slow down your reactions
(c) are used as painkillers
(d) cause hallucinations   (1 mark)

4 Stimulants are drugs that
(a) make you alert and awake
(b) are used as painkillers
(c) are not harmful
(d) slow down your reactions   (1 mark)

5 The effects of solvents are similar to which other drug?
(a) sedatives
(b) smoking
(c) alcohol
(d) stimulants   (1 mark)

Score /5

B **Answer all parts of the question.**

1 Match up these facts with the following drugs

sedatives | hallucinogens | painkillers | stimulants | alcohol | solvents | cigarettes

Facts

(a) A depressant that slows the body's reactions. It causes a disease called cirrhosis.

(b) It contains many harmful chemical substances and is very addictive. It contributes to a disease called emphysema.

(c) This drug can give you extreme energy and also dehydration. It causes you to imagine things that are not really there.

(d) They slows down the brain and alter reaction times. They can be used to treat stress and anxiety.

(e) It speeds up the brain and nervous system, addiction is high and withdrawal has many side effects including depression.

(f) This drug is used to treat pain, misuse can lead to infectious diseases and it is extremely addictive.

(g) This drug affects the lungs, brain, kidney and liver. It can cause loss of control and unconsciousness.   (7 marks)

Score /7

Letts

BRAND NEW

GCSE

VISUAL
REVISION
GUIDE

SUCCESS

QUESTIONS & ANSWERS

BIOLOGY

Hannah Kingston

ANSWER BOOK

THE DIGESTIVE SYSTEM

Section A
1 (a)
2 (c)
3 (d)
4 (b)
5 (c)

Section B
1 In order from top to bottom, small intestine, gall bladder, liver, pancreas, stomach

2

Feature	Saliva	Gastric juice	Pancreatic juice
Slightly alkaline	✔	✗	✔
produced by the stomach	✗	✔	✗
contain a protease	✗	✔	✔
contains lipase	✗	✗	✔

Section C
1 (a) A = stomach
    B = liver
    C = small intestine
    D = large intestine
  (b) (i) liver/B
    (ii) stomach/A
    (iii) small intestine/C
    (iv) large intestine/D
2 Bile breaks down fats into droplets (1 mark) called emulsification (1 mark) so that lipase has a larger surface area to work on (1 mark) to digest them completely.

HELP WITH DIGESTION

Section A
1 (b)
2 (a)
3 (d)
4 (c)
5 (d)

Section B

Part of the digestive system	Enzyme used	Nutrient digested	products
mouth	amylase	starch	sugars
stomach	pepsin	protein	amino acids
small intestine	lipase	lipids	fatty acids and glycerol

2 (a) Correct temperature and acidic conditions
  (b) Water and salts are removed (1 mark) It is then turned into faeces (1 mark) and removed via the anus (1 mark)

Section C
1 (a) (i) the small intestine wall
    (ii) the blood
    (iii) the contents of the small intestine
  (b) (i) no starch, no glucose
    (ii) starch, no glucose
  (c) (i) no starch, glucose
    (ii) no starch, glucose

(d) At the beginning starch is too large a molecule to pass through the visking tubing.(1 mark) Amylase breaks it down into glucose (1 mark) which is small enough to pass through (1 mark)
2 (a) Our food is large and insoluble (1 mark) so it has to be digested into small soluble molecules (1 mark) then it can be absorbed into the blood through the small intestine wall (1 mark).

NUTRITION AND FOOD TESTS

Section A
1 (c)
2 (b)
3 (a)
4 (d)
5 (a)

Section B
1

Nutrient	Use in body	Symptom of deficiency
iron	making haemoglobin	anaemia
calcium	bones and teeth	rickets
vitamin D	absorption of calcium	rickets
vitamin C	skin and blood vessels	scurvy

2 Carbohydrates = energy
Fats = store of energy, making cell membranes
Protein = growth and repair and replacement of cells

Section C
1 (a) pasta and potatoes
  (b) They contain a lot of carbohydrate which gives you energy.
  (c) Fibre helps food move through the digestive system. One effect of lack of fibre is constipation/difficulty in going to the toilet.
  (d) vitamins, minerals and water
2 (a) (i) Use iodine. A positive result is a colour change from yellow to a blue/black colour. (2 marks)
    (ii) Add Benedict's solution and heat. A positive result is a colour change to orange from blue. (3 marks)
    (iii) Add Biuret's solution (copper sulphate and sodium hydroxide). A positive result is a colour change from light blue to purple. (2 marks)

CIRCULATION

Section A
1 (b)
2 (a)
3 (c)
4 (d)
5 (a)

Section B
1 (a) true, (b) false, (c) false, (d) true
2 Right atrium, lungs, pulmonary vein, left ventricle, aorta

Section C
1 (a) Lungs
  (b) It gets picked up by the red blood cells/diffuses into the blood.
  (c) It diffuses/passes out of the blood into the body organs.
  (d) diffusion
  (e) vena cava or pulmonary artery as the oxygen has been dropped off at the body and it is on its way to collect more at the lungs.
2 right ventricle, pulmonary artery, lungs, pulmonary vein, left atrium, left ventricle, aorta, body back to the heart via the vena cava

BLOOD

Section A
1 (b)
2 (a)
3 (c)
4 (d)
5 (a)

Section B
(a) A = red blood cell,
    B = lymphocyte/white blood cell,
    C = platelets,
    D = plasma.
(b) (i) plasma/D
    (ii) platelets/ C
    (iii) red blood cell/A
    (iv) lymphocyte/B

Section C
1 (a) carbon dioxide, soluble food, salts, urea, hormones, antibodies, plasma proteins (any two)
  (b) (i) It is carried by haemoglobin in the red blood cells and forms oxyhaemoglobin.
    (ii) large surface area, no nucleus
  (c) The clots prevent microbes from entering the body.
  (d) (i) ingest bacteria
    (ii) produce antibodies
2 (a) As altitude increases, the number of red blood cells present in people increases.
  (b) At high altitude oxygen levels are lower. Having more red blood cells enables them to carry more oxygen to compensate.

HEART OF THE MATTER

Section A
1 (b)
2 (a)
3 (c)
4 (d)
5 (a)

Section B

Statement	Arteries	Veins	Capillaries
carries blood at high pressure	✔		
carries blood at low pressure		✔	
has valves		✔	

carries blood away from organs		✔	
carries blood rich in carbon dioxide to the heart		✔	
has walls that are one cell thick			✔
allows substances to pass through walls			✔
usually carries oxygenated blood	✔		
supplies the heart with oxygen and nutrients	✔		
are in close contact with body cells			✔
has thick elastic walls	✔		

Section C
1. (a) muscle
   (b) contract and pump blood around the body
   (c) for respiration/ to make energy
   (d) get less/stopped, heart will be starved of oxygen and not produce energy, leading to a heart attack
   (e) Don't smoke, Take exercise and eat a healthy diet
2. (a) A = atriums
   B = ventricles
   C = valves (semi–lunar)
   (b) to prevent the blood flowing backwards

THE BREATHING SYSTEM

Section A
1. (b)
2. (c)
3. (a)
4. (b)
5. (b)

Section B
1. (f), (b), (c), (d), (a), (e)
2. (a) True,
   (b) true,
   (c) false,
   (d) false,
   (e) true

Section C
1. (a) large surface area, moist, thin walls, lots of alveoli air sacs, surrounded by blood capillaries (any three)
   (b) The intercostal muscles contract, the ribs move up and out, the diaphragm contracts and is pulled down, the volume inside the thorax increases and the pressure falls, air is drawn in (any six for 1 mark each)

(c) oxygen and carbon dioxide
(d) The cells lining the respiratory system (trachea/windpipe) make mucus (1 mark), which trap the dust and bacteria.(1 mark) Cilia/tiny hairs on the cells waft them all up to the mouth out of the lungs. (1 mark)
(e) Air breathed out is warmer, contains more water vapour and more carbon dioxide. (any two)

RESPIRATION

Section A
1. (a)
2. (b)
3. (c)
4. (a)
5. (d)

Section B
1. 1. = glucose
   2. = oxygen
   3. = mitochondria
   4. = carbon dioxide
   5. = water
   6. = energy
2. making muscles work, moving molecules against a concentration gradient, chemical reactions, growth and repair of cells, building up large molecules, maintaining body temperature (any four)

Section C
1. (a) 20mg/100cm3
   (b) 60mg/100cm3
   (c) 45 minutes
   (d) anaerobic respiration
   (e) vigorous exercise
   (f) the increased amount of oxygen needed is to repay the oxygen debt. More oxygen is needed to completely break down glucose into carbon dioxide and water.
2. (a) glucose → energy + lactic acid
   (b) Anaerobic respiration in yeast produces alcohol, in humans it is lactic acid

NERVOUS SYSTEM

Section A
1. (c)
2. (a)
3. (b)
4. (d)
5. (a)

Section B
1. false, false, true, true, false
2. relay neurone – connects two neurones together
   sensory neurone –receives messages from the sense organs
   motor neurone –sends messages to a muscle or a gland

Section C
1. (a) A = sensory neurone
   B = relay neurone
   C = motor neurone
   D = muscle
   (b) arrow from B to C, arrow from C to D
   (c) synapse
   (d) by chemical transmitters
2. (a) (i) blink
       (ii) cough
       (iii) pupils get smaller
       (iv) produce saliva
   (b) reflex

THE EYE

Section A
1. (b)
2. (a)
3. (c)
4. (d)
5. (a)

Section B
1. A = sclera
   B = cornea
   C = iris
   D = pupil
2. (a) Retina,
   (b) iris,
   (c) lens,
   (d) pupil,
   (e) sclera,
   (f) cornea

Section C
1. (a) Cornea, curved and clear
   (b) light from the object enters the eye through the curved cornea (1 mark) the ciliary muscles contract (1 mark) the suspensory ligaments slacken (1 mark) the lens gets fatter and rounder (1 mark) light gets bent a lot and gets focused on the retina (1mark)
2. (a) The iris controls the pupil size.
   (b) (i) in bright light
       (ii) in dim light

CELLS

Section A
1. (a)
2. (b)
3. (d)
4. (b)
5. (a)

Section B
1. sperm cell, nerve cell, red blood cell
2. (a) True,
   (b) false,
   (c) false,
   (d) false,
   (e) true,
   (f) false,
   (g) true

Section C
1. (a) A = sperm cell,
   B = phagocyte (white blood cell),
   C = nerve cell,
   D = ciliated cell,
   E = muscle cell.
   (b) (i) A
       (ii) D
       (iii) C
       (iv) D
       (v) B
   (c) To contract and move muscles
2. (a) A plant cell has a cell wall, vacuole and chloroplasts animal cells do not.
   (b) Root hair cell, guard cell, palisade cell mesophyll cell, xylem (any three)

DIFFUSION, OSMOSIS AND ACTIVE TRANSPORT

Section A
1. (c)
2. (b)
3. (a)
4. (d)
5. (c)

Section B

1 (a) From B to A (b) osmosis

2

	Diffusion	Osmosis	Active transport
Molecules move from high to low concentration	✔	✔	✗
Movement requires energy	✗	✗	✔
Molecules travel against the concentration gradient	✗	✗	✔
Movement takes place in animal and plant cells	✔	✔	✔

Section C

1 (a) 6 correct plots, neatly plotted, joined by a straight line
   (b) (i) 0% and 2%
      (ii) Concentration of water is more concentrated outside the cell, so water moves in by osmosis from a high to low concentration, causing the potato cell to gain mass.
   (c) (i) 0.2/5 x 100 = 4%
      (ii) Water moves from a higher concentration inside the potato to a low concentration outside by osmosis causing the potato to lose mass
   (d) (i) 4 %
      (ii) The concentration of water was the same inside the potato and outside the potato so there was no net movement of water by osmosis (answers should imply that water still moves in both directions).

PLANT AND LEAF

Section A

1 (c)
2 (a)
3 (b)
4 (b)
5 (d)

Section B

1 (a) root hairs,
   (b) leaf,
   (c) flower,
   (d) root,
   (e) stem
2 controls the opening and closing of stomata = guard cells
   allows gases to circulate = spongy layer
   contains xylem and phloem = leaf = vein
   contains many chloroplasts = palisade layer
   allows carbon dioxide in = stomata

Section C

1 (a) (i) F
      (ii) A
      (iii) D
      (iv) C
      (v) B
      (vi) E

   (b) A = waxy cuticle,
      B = spongy layer,
      C = guard cell,
      D = stomata,
      E = leaf, vein,
      F = palisade cell,
   (c) (i) anchor the plant in the soil
      (ii) absorb water and minerals from the soil
      (iii) keep the plant upright
2 Water is absorbed by the root hairs into the root and up the stem to the leaf in xylem vessels.

PLANT SENSES

Section A

1 (b)
2 (a)
3 (c)
4 (d)
5 (c)

Section B

1 (a) (i) hydrotropism
      (ii) geotropism
      (iii) phototropism
   (b) plant leaning towards the light
   (c) hormone collects on the opposite side of the plant to the light

Section C

1 (a) unequal distribution of hormone
   (b) shaded hormone on the lower part of the shoot and the lower part of the root
   (c) (i) It slows down the growth of cells on the side it collects.
      (ii) It Speeds up the growth of cells on the side it collects.
   (d) (i) They grow towards the light.
      (ii) The roots grow towards water .
      (iii) The shoot grows up and the root grows down due to gravity.
2 Growing cuttings to stimulate root growth, killing weeds, early ripening of fruit, producing seedless fruit (any 3)

PLANT TRANSPORT AND GOOD HEALTH

Section A

1 (a)
2 (d)
3 (b)
4 (c)
5 (a)

Section B

1 (a) loss, evaporation
   (b) light, temperature, air
   (c) hot, dry, windy
2 Correct words = flaccid, turgid, phloem, xylem

Section C

1 (a) The roots need oxygen for respiration b) to prevent algae growing that would use up the minerals
   (c) length or number of leaves
   (d) (i) stunted growth, yellow older leaves
      (ii) yellow leaves with dead spots (iii) poor root growth and purple younger leaves
      (2 marks for each part)

PHOTOSYNTHESIS

Section A

1 (c)
2 (d)
3 (b)
4 (c)
5 (d)

Section B

1 (a) Making cell walls
   (b) Nitrates
   (c) dissolved in water in the soil, absorbed by the root hairs
   (d) starch is insoluble and does not affect osmosis
   (e) glucose
   (f) respiration

Section C

1 (a) carbon dioxide
   (b) light or temperature
   (c) increasing amounts of carbon dioxide increases the rate of photosynthesis up to a maximum of 0.3%
   (d) more carbon dioxide and more warmth means more growth
   (e) clean windows to allow light through, enough minerals, enough warmth (any two)

THE SKIN

Section A

1 (b)
2 (c)
3 (a)
4 (c)
5 (a)

Section B

1 Correct words = dilate, more, start, flat, radiation
2 False, true, true, false, true

Section C

1 (a) They constrict, called vasoconstriction.
   (b) Less blood gets to the surface of the skin, less heat is lost by radiation and body temperature returns to normal.
   (c) Muscles contract and carry out respiration to produce heat energy to warm the body.
   (d) Sweating produces water on the surface of the skin, the water evaporates taking away heat energy as it does so, returning the body temperature to normal.
   (e) Take off clothes = less insulation. Vasodilate arterioles= more heat lost by radiation.

THE KIDNEYS 1

Section A

1 (a)
2 (b)
3 (d)
4 (c)
5 (d)

Section B

1 (a) = lungs, skin, kidneys
   (b) = skin, kidneys
   (c) = lungs, kidneys
   (d) = kidneys
   (e) = skin
1 All three (must have all three to gain mark) skin and kidneys, (must have both to gain mark) lungs, kidneys, skin
2 A = renal artery B = renal vein C = Bladder D = ureter E = urethra f = kidney G = vena cava H = aorta

Section C

1 (a) (i) same (ii) less (iii) less (iv) less
   (b) It is reabsorbed into the blood
2 (a) 3cm^3/min
   (b) Urine production is increased
   (c) If blood becomes concentrated (1 mark), ADH is secreted (1 mark) which causes

the kidney to absorb more water from the blood,(1 mark) less water is secreted in the urine (1 mark) and blood concentration returns to normal. (1 mark)

THE KIDNEYS 2

Section A
1 (b)
2 (c)
3 (a)
4 (b)
5 (c)

Section B
1 (a) false,
   (b) false,
   (c) true,
   (d) true,
   (e) true,
   (f) true,
   (g) false,
   (h) true,
   (i) true.
2 (b), (e), (c), (d), (a)

Section C
1 (a) glucose
   (b) useful for the body
   (c) the liver, excess amino acids
   (d) 50 – 10 = 40g
   (e) 40 – 30 = 10g
   (f) 150 – 1.5 = 148.5litres
2 (a) ADH (b) glucose (c) urea

CAUSES OF DISEASE

Section A
1 (a)
2 (b)
3 (d)
4 (c)
5 (a)

Section B
1 (a)
   (b) They are all caused by bacteria

Name of disease	microbe	method of spread	method of treatment
Polio	virus	air and water	immunisation
Measles	virus	air	immunisation
Chicken Pox	virus	air	immunisation
Tetanus	bacteria	infected cuts	immunisation
Tuberculosis	bacteria	air	immunisation
Food Poisoning	bacteria	contaminated food	antibiotics
Pneumonia	bacteria	air	antibiotics

Section C
1 (a) Viruses and fungi
   (b) Consists of a cell wall surrounding a cell membrane. The cytoplasm contains genes not in a nucleus.
   (c) Bacterial cell is larger, both have genes, virus has a protein coat not a cell wall (any two)
2 (a) Reproduce rapidly in the body. (1 mark), destroy living tissue (1 mark), produce

toxins/poisons (1 mark), reproduce inside cells (1 mark), kill cell in the process. (1mark)
   (b) Respiratory, digestive, reproductive system and broken skin.

DEFENCE AGAINST DISEASE

Section A
1 (a)
2 (b)
3 (d)
4 (c)
5 (a)

Section B
1 (a) blood, (b) skin, (c) lungs, (d) stomach, (e) eyes
2 (a) false, (b) false, (c) false, (d) true, (e) true

Section C
1 (a) (i) D
       (ii) E
   (b) Antibiotics diffuse into the agar and kill the bacteria.
   (c) In case all of the bacteria had not been destroyed.
   (d) Measles is a virus and cannot be treated with antibiotics.
2 (a) Ingests microbes, produce antibodies or antitoxins.
   (b) White blood cells have a memory, so if re-infection occurs they make antibodies much faster before the person gets any symptoms, so that they are immune to the disease.

DRUGS, SOLVENTS, ALCOHOL AND TOBACCO

Section A
1 (c)
2 (a)
3 (d)
4 (a)
5 (c)

Section B
1 (a) alcohol,
   (b) cigarettes,
   (c) hallucinogens,
   (d) sedatives,
   (e) stimulants,
   (f) painkillers,
   (g) solvents.
2 (a) heroin,
   (b) morphine,
   (c) ecstasy,
   (d) cannabis,
   (e) amphetamine

Section C
1 (a) Reaction time increases the more alcohol there is in the blood.
   (b) Alcohol in the blood makes the driver have slower reactions therefore would not be able to react in time to avoid an accident.
   (c) It doubled.
   (d) Cirrhosis of the liver, depression, addiction (any two)
2 (a) (i)   Addictive, blocks arteries.
       (ii)   Prevents the red blood cells from carrying oxygen (1 mark for each harmful effect, max. 3 marks total)
       (iii) Contains carcinogens that cause cancer, affects breathing, damages cilia, causes cell mutations.

HORMONES AND DIABETES

Section A
1 (a)
2 (b)
3 (d)
4 (c)
5 (a)

Section B
1 (a) testes, (b) ovaries,
   (c) pancreas, (d) pancreas,
   (e) brain, (f) brain
2 pancreas, glycogen, lowers, glucagon, glycogen, diabetes

Section C
1

Gland	Hormone	Involved in
pituitary	ADH, FSH, LH	menstrual cycle, water regulation
thyroid	thyroxine	growth
adrenal	adrenaline	fight or flight
testes	testosterone	puberty
ovaries	oestrogen/ progesterone	puberty
pancreas	insulin	control of blood sugar

2 (a) Both involve a stimulus, an organ that responds and a response.
   (b) Hormonal travels in the blood, nervous via neurones. Hormonal is slower than nervous. Hormonal is chemical, nervous is electrical.

THE MENSTRUAL CYCLE

Section A
1 (a)
2 (c)
3 (d)
4 (b)
5 (b)

Section B
1 ovulation — the release of an egg
   progesterone — maintains the uterus lining
   oestrogen — inhibits the production of FSH
   luteinising hormone — causes the release of an egg
   follicle stimulating hormone — begins the menstrual cycle
2 28 days, ovulation, hormones, pituitary gland, progesterone, ovaries

Section C
1 (a) pituitary
   (b) (i) A = follicle stimulating hormone
      (ii) B = oestrogen/progesterone
      (iii) C = oestrogen
   (c) Increases the blood supply, maintains its thickness
   (d) Oestrogen inhibits FSH, no inhibition means more eggs will develop to have a chance of fertilisation.
   (e) Luteinising hormone causes the release of an egg(ovulation) and stimulates the release of progesterone.

(f) If hormone B is oestrogen, then a type of hormone that would keep this high would mean that FSH is inhibited, so no eggs are released. If hormone B was progesterone, then keeping this hormone high would maintain the uterus lining. Both would prevent pregnancy.

VARIATION

Section A
1 (b)
2 (b)
3 (a)
4 (c)
5 (d)

Section B
1 (a) Graph should be the shape of a continuous variation graph (A)
   (b) Graph should be the shape of a discontinuous variation graph (have distinct groups) (B)

A

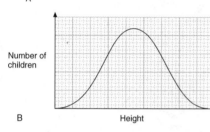

Number of children — Height

B

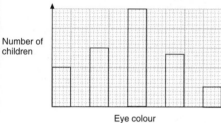

Number of children — Eye colour

2 (i) Graph A (ii) Graph B

Section C
1 (a) 20–45 cm
   (b) 17/20 x 100 = 85%
   (c) The environment had an effect on them, e.g. some had less water/nutrients; competition, disease, temperature, different soil types, different amounts of light (any two)
   (d) Their genes are different (or similar answer involving in inheritance of different colours)
2 (a) asexual
   (b) (i) identical
       (ii) similar but not identical

GENETICS

Section A
1 (b)
2 (a)
3 (c)
4 (d)
5 (a)

Section B
1

recessive	the weaker allele
dominant	the stronger allele
genotype	the type of alleles an organism has
heterozygous	different alleles
homozygous	both alleles the same
phenotype	what an organism physically looks like

2 (a)

	B	b
B	BB	Bb
b	Bb	bb

   (b) Three blue-eyed offspring, one brown-eyed offspring

Section C
1 (a) (i) two different alleles
       (ii) two of the same alleles
   (b) any upper and lower case letter, e.g. S and s genotype of mother = Ss and father = SS
   (c) SS, SS, Ss, Ss
   (d) 1 in 4 answer must be derived from a punnet square to get 4 marks.

	S	s
S	SS	Ss
s	Ss	ss – sufferer

   (e) Are heterozygous for the condition but do not suffer from it.
   (f) in malarial regions as being a carrier means you cannot catch malaria.

GENETIC ENGINEERING

Section A
1 (a)
2 (c)
3 (d)
4 (a)
5 (a)

Section B
1 (a) True, (b) true, (c) false, (d) false, (e) true
2 (e), (d), (c), (b), (a), (f)

Section C
1 (a) Could transfer genes into weeds, may be harmful to humans, may wipe out all other crops that may become useful in the future, as a disease may wipe out all the genetically engineered crops that are the same.
   (b) Plants would obtain nitrate more easily, therefore produce more protein and grow faster, (2 marks) reduce the cost of fertilisers. (1 mark)
   (c) means plants can exploit different soils that are drier; they would also grow with little rainfall in areas, all would mean more crops
   (d) Cut out disease-resistant gene from chromosome of a disease resistant variety, insert into a plant cell, grow plant and clone or use tissue culture.
2 (a) a gene
   (b) A section of DNA is a gene, a gene is a sequence of bases. The sequence of bases determines the order of amino acids that make up a protein. Different genes (sequence of bases) code for different proteins.

INHERITED DISEASES

Section A
1 (b)
2 (a)
3 (b)
4 (b)
5 (c)

Section B
1 (a) HH, or Hh
   (b) father = Hh mother = hh (2 marks)
       gametes H, h h, h (2 marks)

	H	h
h	Hh	hh
h	Hh	hh

   (4 marks)
   phenotypes = 2 sufferers 2 normal (2 marks)

Section C
1 (a) (i) cc
       (ii) Cc
       (iii) CC
   (b) thick sticky mucus on the lungs, difficulty breathing, prone to bacterial chest infections
   (c) inheritance from BOTH parents
2 (a) Cc
   (b) CC
   (c) normal
   (d) (i) 25% or 1 in 4
       (ii) 50% or 2 in 4

MITOSIS

Section A
1 (a)
2 (c)
3 (c)
4 (b)
5 (a)

Section B
1 (a) 46 (b) 46 (c) 2 (d) identical
2 Two daughter cells exactly the same as the parent cell

Section C
1 (a) They duplicate, separate into two with one set of chromosomes in each cell
   (b) A = meiosis,
       B = fertilisation,
       C = mitosis,
   (c) Top line = 46,
       second line = 23,
       third line = 46,
       fourth line = 46,
       (1 mark for each cell)
2 (a) growth and replacement of cells
   (b) vegetative propagation/cloning/taking cuttings
   (c) quick, cheap, can grow plants with special qualities such as resistance to a disease or all the same colour, etc.

MEIOSIS AND FERTILISATION

Section A
1 (a)
2 (c)
3 (b)
4 (d)
5 (a)

Section B
1 Gametes, half, 46, egg, sperm
2 (a) XX (b) XY (c) 50% 1 in 2
   (d) The Y chromosome is smaller.

Section C
1 (a) The sex chromosomes
   (b) A fertilised egg
   (c) Meiosis
   (d) (i) 23 (ii) 46
   (e) (i) process 2 (ii) process 1
   (f) 50 % / 2 in 4

		male	
		X	Y
female	X	XX	XY
	X	XX	XY

   (1 mark for answer all three marks for answer and correct punnet square diagram)

GENES, CHROMOSOMES AND MUTATIONS

Section A
1 (b)
2 (a)
3 (c)
4 (d)
5 (c)

Section B
1 (a) (i) 400 (ii) 800 (iii) 800
  (b) They have no nucleus.
2 (a) true, (b) false, (c) false,
  (d) true, (e) true

Section C
1 (a) the change in a chemical structure of a gene or a chromosome which changes the way an organism develops.
  (b) The percentage of mutations increases with increasing doses of radiation.
  (c) UV light/alpha/beta/gamma radiation/radioactivity/smoking/drugs /chemicals, random/natural copying error during growth
  (d) Mutation had occurred in the body cells, therefore not inherited.
2 (a) The nucleus contains chromosomes, which are made up of DNA. A gene is a section of DNA.
  (1 mark each)

SELECTIVE BREEDING

Section A
1 (c)
2 (a)
3 (b)
4 (a)
5 (d)

Section B
1

artificial selection	a term used for selective breeding
tissue culture	growing plants from a plant cells
artificial insemination	female inseminating animal with sperm
Selective breeding	breeding in desirable characteristics

2 (a) Asexual reproduction produces clones and only needs one parent, sexual reproduction produces variation and needs two parents.
  (b) Artificial selection is when humans decide who will breed, natural selection is when nature decides who will breed and survive.
  (c) quick, cheap and it produces identical copies of a desirable plant.

Section C
1 (a) variation
  (b) Grow seeds, select best apples, breed together, repeat for many generations until all apples were large and tasty. (1 mark each)
  (c) asexual (not cloning)
  (d) to produce clones/ identical copies
2 (a) artificial selection
  (b) If plants and animals are all the same and a disease affects them then it would wipe out all of them. Older varieties showing variation would survive. Continual selective breeding reduces the variation and leads to a reduction in the number of alleles.

THE CARBON CYCLE

Section A
1 (c)
2 (a)
3 (d)
4 (b)
5 (a)

Section B
1 photosynthesis, eat, respiration, waste, die, decomposers, decomposers, fossil fuels, pressure, fossil fuels
2 (a) warmth, moisture and oxygen
  (b) 0.30 %

Section C
1 (a) Carbon Dioxide
  (b) 1. photosynthesis 2. respiration 3. eating 4. burning/combustion
  (c) Plants take in carbon from the atmosphere and use it for photosynthesis; they incorporate the carbon into their bodies; animals eat the plants to get their carbon; both die; the bodies are broken down by decomposers into the soil.
  (d) decomposers bacteria and fungi
  (e) Turns into fossil fuels, coal, oil and gas and is released back into the air when they are used as fuels.

NITROGEN CYCLE

Section A
1 (b)
2 (a)
3 (d)
4 (c)
5 (b)

Section B
1 (a) false, (b) false, (c) true,
  (d) true, (e) true, (f) false,
  (g) false, (h) true, (i) true,
  (j) true
2 (a) They contain nitrogen fixing bacteria in their root nodules that turn nitrogen into nitrates

Section C
1 (a) A = nitrates,
    B = ammonium compounds/ammonia
  (b) nitrifying bacteria
  (c) dissolved in water and taken up during photosynthesis
  (d) Use fertilisers, grow leguminous plants and plough them into the soil, thus increasing the amount of nitrogen-fixing bacteria in the soil.
  (e) Plants and animals die; decayed by micro-organisms/denitrifying bacteria; which release nitrogen back into the atmosphere; in waterlogged soils/anaerobic conditions.

FOOD CHAINS AND WEBS

Section A
1 (d)
2 (a)
3 (a)
4 (a)
5 (c)

Section B
1

2 These numbers would decrease due to lack of food

Section C
  (a) 150kJ
  (b) 70kJ
  (c) 150/1000 x 100 = 15%
  (d) movement, keeping warm, faeces, respiration, incorporated into their bodies
  (e) energy loss, not enough energy to sustain more levels
  (f) Light doesn't strike grass. Light wrong wavelength. Light is reflected. Light misses chlorophyll molecule. (any two)

PYRAMIDS OF NUMBERS AND BIOMASS

Section A
1 (d)
2 (a)
3 (b)
4 (a)
5 (a)

Section B
1 Correct inverted pyramid, 1 rose bush then 20 caterpillars then 5 thrushes (1 mark). Labelling the pyramid the bars drawn in proportion to the numbers (1 mark)
2 1 mark for the correct shape pyramid, 1 mark for labels, 1 mark for correct length of bars in proportion 1 mark for correct calculation. Rose bush = 500g caterpillars = 20 x 4g = 80g and thrush = 5 x 70g = 350g

Section C
1 (a) 1 mark for labels, 1 mark for correctly proportioned pyramid i.e. lengths of bars proportional to the numbers, 1 mark for pyramid in the correct order (Plant plankton at the bottom, then animal plankton, then mackerel, then human)
  (b) an organism's dry mass
  (c) (i) increase/grow more
    (ii) decrease in numbers
  (d) overfished, not enough food, disease, competition, predators (any two)
  (e) reduce fishing, breed in captivity and release, introduce quotas, avoid fishing in breeding areas, don't catch small fish (any two)

EVOLUTION

Section A
1 (b)
2 (c)
3 (a)
4 (c)
5 (a)

Section B
1 (a) They were no longer camouflaged so were eaten by predators
  (b) in the cleaner areas, the countryside
  (c) A mutation caused them to change in order to survive the pollution on the trees.
  (d) natural selection

Section C
1 (a) an increase in the number of species
  (b) The number of species was constantly rising, then fell, then rose again.
  (c) competition, predators, unable to adapt to the changing environment, disease (any one)
2 (a) (i) too cold (ii) too hot/not enough moisture (iii) no oxygen

(b) Organisms have changed/adapted and improved in response to the change in climate and conditions over time and formed new species.

(c) natural selection

ADAPTATION AND COMPETITION

Section A
1 (a)
2 (d)
3 (c)
4 (d)
5 (a)

Section B
1 ability to store water, extensive root system, no leaves so less water lost by evaporation through the stomata, strong roots to anchor in the sand
2 competition, disease, amount of food and water, predators, climate change, human activity (any three)
3 (a) an animal that hunts
   (b) the hunted animal

Section C
1 (a) falls, increases, falls again.
   (b) eaten by the owls, disease, not enough food, competition for food, climate change (any one)
   (c) fewer mice to eat
   (d) increase
   (e) Not being eaten so numbers would increase.
   (f) predator–prey cycle

HUMAN INFLUENCE ON THE ENVIRONMENT

Section A
1 (b)
2 (c)
3 (a)
4 (c)
5 (a)

Section B
1 (a) true, (b) false, (c) true,
   (d) true, (e) true, (f) false
2 (a) the chopping down of trees
   (b) trees are no longer absorbing carbon dioxide so levels rise
   (c) soil erosion, less rainfall, destruction of habitats
   (any 2)

Section C
1 (a) For : use less insecticide, cost less. Against: not fully tested may have long-term effects. May affect ecosystems and get into food chains.
2 (a) Sewage contains nitrates which are fertilisers. That increases plant growth.
   (b) Plants die due to competition; microbes feed on the plants; oxygen is used up by the microbes during respiration; fish/animals die due to lack of oxygen.
   (c) Eutrophication

ACID RAIN, POLLUTION AND THE GREENHOUSE EFFECT

Section A
1 (a)
2 (d)
3 (a)
4 (c)
5 (b)

Section B
1 The gases dissolve in the clouds, wind blows the clouds, rain falls in another part of the country.
2 Greenhouse effect, sulphur dioxide, global warming, suns, energy, deforestation, ozone layer

Section C
1 (a) carbon dioxide and methane
   (b) (i) Increases the amount of carbon dioxide as not absorbed by trees.
       (ii) Rice fields produce methane.
       (iii) Releases carbon dioxide into the air.
   (c) The Earth's temperature is rising due to the Greenhouse effect.
   (d) rise in temperature/climate change; rise in sea level, melting of the polar ice caps; flooding (any two)
2 (a) Industrialisation means more is burnt; a build-up over the years; burning more to cope with increase in population
   (b) sulphur dioxide, various nitrogen oxides

BIOTECHNOLOGY

Section A
1 (b)
2 (a)
3 (d)
4 (a)
5 (b)

Section B
1 (a) True, (b) false, (c) true,
   (d) false, (e) true, (f) true.
2 (a) fermenter vessesl (b) pH, temperature, oxygen levels, substrate levels, sterility (any three)

Section C
1 (a) Fermentation vessel
   (b) Products are recycled and only collected when it reaches the right strength.
   (c) To keep the bacteria supplied with oxygen
   (d) Respiration generates heat
   (e) Use a cooling jacket, circulate water around the vessel. If it gets too hot, the enzymes involved in the process are denatured/stop working, too much heat would kill microbes.
   (f) to prevent unwanted microbes from entering
   (g) Vinegar is acidic, need to get the right pH of vinegar.

LETTS EDUCATIONAL
The Chiswick Centre
414 Chiswick High Road
London W4 5TF
Tel: 020 8996 3333
Fax: 020 8742 8390
Email: mail@lettsed.co.uk
Website: www.letts-education.com

C These are GCSE-style questions. Answer all parts of the questions.

1 The graph shows the effect of different amounts of alcohol on the mean reaction time of a group of people.

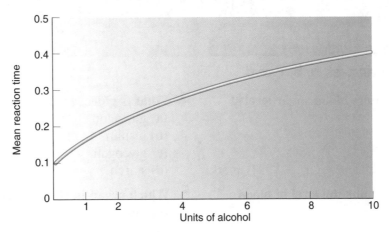

(a) What is the relationship between the reaction time and the amount of alcohol in the blood?

.... (1 mark)

(b) Using the information in the graph, explain why it is dangerous to drink and drive.

....

.... (2 marks)

(c) What has happened to the reaction time between 0 and 2 units of alcohol?

.... (1 mark)

(d) Name two other effects of alcohol on the body.

....

.... (2 marks)

2 Tobacco smoke contains many chemicals. Three of them are named below. Explain briefly why they are harmful.

(a) nicotine

....

(b) carbon monoxide

....

(c) tar

.... (3 marks)

Score   /9

How well did you do?

0–5 correct Try again
6–11 correct Getting there
12–16 correct Good work
17–21 correct Excellent!

TOTAL SCORE   /21

For more on this topic
see pages 46–47 of your Success Guide

HORMONES AND DIABETES

A

Choose just one answer, a, b, c or d.

1 Which organ monitors blood sugar levels?
(a) the brain
(b) the heart
(c) the kidneys
(d) the pancreas   (1 mark)

2 Which organ maintains the level of blood glucose?
(a) the heart
(b) the pancreas
(c) the brain
(b) the kidneys   (1 mark)

3 Which hormone is secreted if blood sugar level is high?
(a) glycogen   (c) glucagon
(b) adrenaline   (d) insulin   (1 mark)

4 What is glucose stored as in animals?
(a) glucagon
(b) insulin
(c) glycogen
(d) starch   (1 mark)

5 Which organ in the body makes progesterone?
(a) ovaries
(b) testes
(c) brain
(d) liver   (1 mark)

Score   /5

B

Answer all parts of the questions.

1 Match the organs with the hormone they produce.

| ovaries | | testes | | pancreas | | brain |

(a) testosterone ....

(b) oestrogen ....

(c) insulin ....

(d) glucagon ....

(e) ADH ....

(f) FSH ....   (6 marks)

2 Fill in the gaps.

Insulin is a hormone produced by the .... It works by stimulating the body cells to take up glucose from the blood and causes the liver to convert glucose to storage .... This .... the blood sugar level to normal. If blood sugar level falls below normal, another hormone is released called .... This works by causing the liver to convert .... back into glucose and increases sugar levels to normal. The illness .... results when the pancreas doesn't make enough insulin.   (6 marks)

Score   /12

50

C

These are GCSE-style questions. Answer all parts of the questions.

1 Complete the following table showing some hormones, where they are produced and their effects.

Gland	Hormone	Involved in
pituitary	ADH, FSH, LH	menstrual cycle, water regulation
thyroid		growth
adrenal		fight or flight
testes		puberty
ovaries		puberty
	insulin	

(6 marks)

2 The diagrams below show an outline of nervous and hormonal co-ordination.

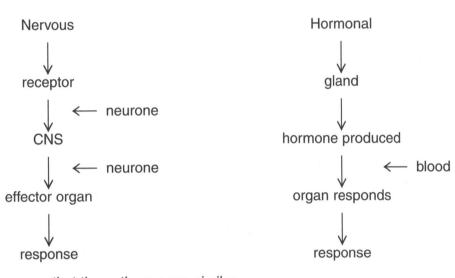

(a) Give three ways that the pathways are similar.

....

....

....

(3 marks)

(b) Give three ways that they are different.

....

....

....

(3 marks)

Score   /12

How well did you do?

0–7 correct Try again
8–14 correct Getting there
15–22 correct Good work
23–29 correct Excellent!

TOTAL SCORE   /29

**For more on this topic
see pages 48–49 of your Success Guide**

THE MENSTRUAL CYCLE

A

Choose just one answer, a, b, c or d.

1 Which of the following hormones starts the menstrual cycle?
(a) follicle stimulating hormone
(b) progesterone
(c) luteinising hormone
(d) oestrogen   (1 mark)

2 On which day does an egg get released from the ovary?
(a) day 11   (c) day 14
(b) day 5   (d) day 28   (1 mark)

3 Why does the uterus lining thicken in the menstrual cycle?
(a) to stop an egg being released
(b) to prepare for implantation
(c) to protect the vagina
(d) to prepare for menstruation   (1 mark)

4 Which hormone stimulates ovulation?
(a) follicle stimulating hormone
(b) progesterone
(c) oestrogen
(d) luteinising hormone   (1 mark)

5 Which hormone is used in fertility drugs?
(a) testosterone
(b) follicle stimulating hormone
(c) progesterone
(d) oestrogen   (1 mark)

Score   /5

B

Answer all parts of the questions.

1 Match up the correct word(s) with their meaning by drawing single lines.

ovulation   maintains the uterus lining

progesterone   causes the release of an egg

oestrogen   begins the menstrual cycle

luteinising hormone   inhibits the production of FSH

follicle stimulating hormone   the release of an egg

(5 marks)

2 Fill in the gaps.

The menstrual cycle lasts approximately .... It consists of a menstrual bleed and the release of an egg called .... control the whole cycle. Follicle stimulating hormone and luteinising hormone are secreted by the .... in the brain. Oestrogen and .... are secreted by the ....

(6 marks)

Score   /11

52

C These are GCSE-style questions. Answer all parts of the questions.

1 The diagram shows some of the hormones concerned with the female menstrual cycle.

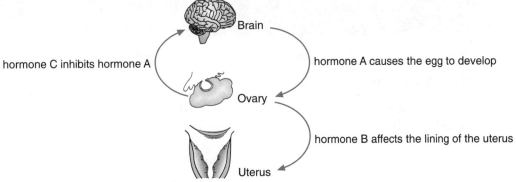

hormone C inhibits hormone A

Brain

hormone A causes the egg to develop

Ovary

hormone B affects the lining of the uterus

Uterus

(a) Name the gland located in the brain that begins the menstrual cycle by secreting a hormone.

.... (1 mark)

(b) Name the hormone

(i) A ....

(ii) B ....

(iii) C .... (3 marks)

(c) How does hormone B affect the uterus lining?

....

.... (2 marks)

(d) A drug called clomiphine can treat some types of infertility. This acts by inhibiting the production of oestrogen. How does this increase the chance of a woman becoming pregnant?

....

.... (2 marks)

(e) Name another hormone involved in the menstrual cycle and explain its effects.

....

.... (2 marks)

(f) One type of hormone keeps the level of hormone B high. Explain how this might work.

....

.... (2 marks)

Score   /12

How well did you do?

0–6 correct   Try again
7–14 correct   Getting there
15–21 correct   Good work
22–28 correct   Excellent!

TOTAL SCORE   /28

For more on this topic
see pages 54–55 of your Success Guide

VARIATION

A Choose just one answer, a, b, c or d.

1 Which of the following is an example of continuous variation?
(a) hair colour
(b) height
(c) eye colour
(d) blood group   (1 mark)

2 Who is affected more by environmental changes?
(a) vertebrates   (c) invertebrates
(b) plants   (d) animals   (1 mark)

3 Which of these is an inherited feature?
(a) blood group
(b) scars
(c) having neat writing
(d) speaking French   (1 mark)

4 Which of these is an inherited example of discontinuous variation?
(a) weight
(b) shoe size
(c) eye colour
(d) height   (1 mark)

5 What causes variation between different animals?
(a) inheritance from one parent only
(b) inheritance from parents only
(c) the environment only
(d) genetics and the environment   (1 mark)

Score   /5

B Answer all parts of the questions.

1 (a) On the diagram below sketch the shape of a graph to show the heights in a typical class of 15 year olds. Label the axis.

A

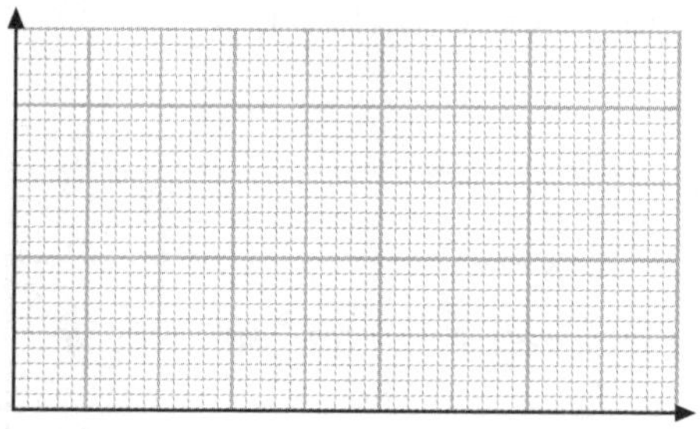

(3 marks)

(b) On the diagram below sketch the shape of a graph to show eye colour in a typical class of 15 year olds. Label the axis.

B

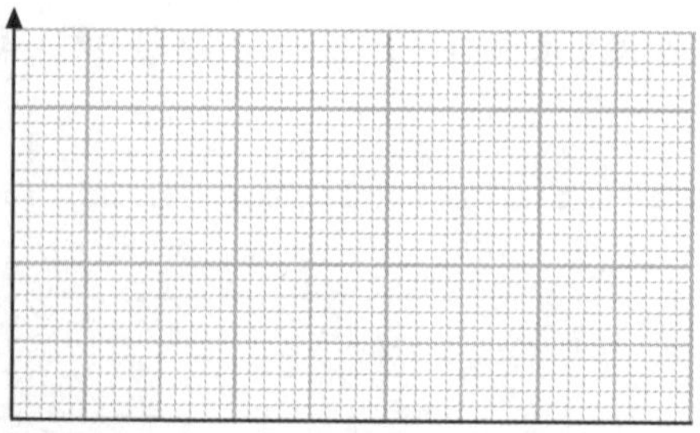

(3 marks)

2 Which of the graphs you have drawn shows

(i) continuous variation ....

(ii) discontinuous variation? .... (2 marks)

Score   /8

C **These are GCSE-style questions. Answer all parts of the questions.**

1 The bar chart shows the range of heights in a sample of daffodils.

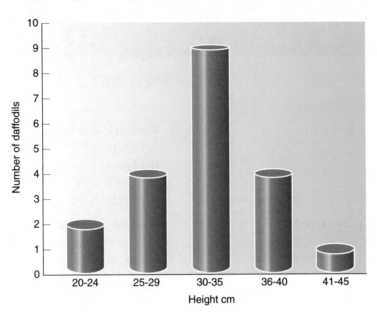

(a) What is the range of heights in this sample?

.... (1 mark)

(b) Calculate the percentage of daffodils between 25 and 40 cm in height.

.... (2 marks)

(c) The daffodils in this sample are from the same species. Why did they grow to different heights?

....

.... (2 marks)

(d) Daffodils from different species show variation in colour. What causes this difference?

.... (1 mark)

2 (a) A species of blackfly can produce eggs without the need for males. What do we call this type of reproduction?

.... (1 mark)

(b) How do the offspring compare?

(i) with each other ....

(ii) with other female blackfly offspring .... (2 marks)

Score   /9

How well did you do?

0–5 correct   Try again
6–11 correct   Getting there
12–17 correct   Good work
18–22 correct   Excellent!

TOTAL SCORE   /22

For more on this topic
see pages 56–57 of your Success Guide

GENETICS

A

Choose just one answer, a, b, c or d.

1 What does recessive mean?
(a) a single allele
(b) a weaker allele
(c) a strong allele
(d) a dominant allele (1 mark)

2 What is a person's phenotype?
(a) what they look like
(b) their dominant genes
(c) what genes they have
(d) their recessive genes (1 mark)

3 What would a person who is heterozygous for eye colour have?
(a) blue genes
(b) two alleles the same
(c) genes that are different
(d) genes that are the same (1 mark)

4 Who discovered the principles of genetics?
(a) Pasteur
(b) Newton
(c) Galileo
(d) Mendel (1 mark)

5 What is monohybrid inheritance?
(a) the inheritance of one characteristic
(b) the inheritance of all characteristics
(c) the inheritance of two characteristics
(d) the study of genetics (1 mark)

Score /5

B

Answer all parts of the questions.

1 Match up the word with its definition by drawing a single line.

recessive	the stronger allele
dominant	what an organism physically looks like
genotype	both alleles the same
heterozygous	the weaker allele
homozygous	the type of alleles an organism has
phenotype	different alleles

(6 marks)

2 (a) Complete the following punnet square. A capital B is the dominant allele for blue eyes, b is the recessive allele for brown eyes.

Genotype   Bb   Bb
Gametes   B,b   B,b

	B	b
B		
b		

(4 marks)

(b) What are the phenotypes of the offspring?

.... (2 marks)

Score /12

C **These are GCSE-style questions. Answer all parts of the questions.**

1 Sickle cell anaemia is an inherited disease of the blood that causes the oxygen–carrying capacity of the blood to be greatly reduced. The condition is caused by a recessive allele.

(a) A mother is heterozygous for the disease and the father is homozygous dominant. What does

   (i) heterozygous mean ....

   (ii) homozygous mean ....   (2 marks)

(b) Choose letters to represent the alleles and state the genotype of the mother and father.

   ....   (3 marks)

(c) What are the four possible genotypes of the mother and father's children? You may use a punnet square diagram in your answer.

   ....

   ....

   ....   (4 marks)

(d) A male and a female both heterozygous decide to have children. What is the probability of a child of theirs suffering from sickle cell anaemia? Use a punnet square diagram in your answer.

   ....

   (4 marks)

(e) The parents in (d) are said to be carriers. What does this mean?

   ....   (1 mark)

(f) When is a carrier of sickle cell at an advantage?

   ....   (2 marks)

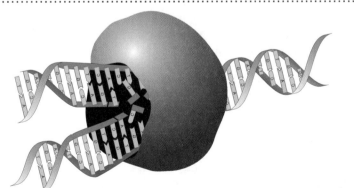

Score   /16

TOTAL SCORE   /33

For more on this topic see pages 58–59 of your Success Guide

GENETIC ENGINEERING

A **Choose just one answer, a, b, c or d.**

1 What do genes code for?
(a) proteins
(b) fats
(c) starch
(d) glucose (1 mark)

2 What are genes made of?
(a) protein
(b) amino acids
(c) DNA
(d) chromosomes (1 mark)

3 Where does protein synthesis begin?
(a) in the vacuole
(b) in the cytoplasm
(c) on the chromosomes
(d) in the nucleus (1 mark)

4 What is the name of the organism used in genetic engineering?
(a) bacteria
(b) fungi
(c) virus
(d) protozoa (1 mark)

5 What do bacteria contain that is used in genetic engineering?
(a) plasmids
(b) genes
(c) nucleus
(d) chromosomes (1 mark)

Score /5

B **Answer all parts of the questions.**

1 True or false?

True False

(a) DNA codes for proteins to be made in the body. ☐ ☐

(b) There is a molecule called RNA involved in making proteins. ☐ ☐

(c) Gene therapy can cure all genetic diseases. ☐ ☐

(d) Fungi is the microbe used in genetic engineering. ☐ ☐

(e) Genetic engineering involves the use of bacteria. ☐ ☐ (5 marks)

2 The following sentences describe one method of making a protein using genetic engineering. Use numbers to put them in the correct order.

(a) Bacteria reproduce rapidly to produce a protein. ....

(b) Bacteria are put into a fermentation vessel. ....

(c) The plasmid is put back into the bacterium. ....

(d) A plasmid from a bacterium is cut open using enzymes and the protein-making gene is inserted. ....

(e) The human gene that codes for a protein is identified and cut out using enzymes. ....

(f) The protein is removed. .... (6 marks)

Score /11

C **These are GCSE-style questions. Answer all parts of the questions.**

1 Scientists have tried to increase food production using genetic engineering. However, this raises concerns with some people.

(a) Outline the risks of genetically engineering crops.

....
....
.... (3 marks)

(b) How could food production be increased if genes that control nitrogen fixation are inserted into crops?

....
....
.... (3 marks)

(c) How could food production be increased if genes were inserted into crops that made them more resistant to drought?

....
.... (2 marks)

(d) Explain how scientists might use genetic engineering to produce crops resistant to a disease.

....
....
.... (4 marks)

2 (a) DNA is a genetic code inside a nucleus; it controls all the characteristics of an individual. DNA can be split into sections. What do we call a section of DNA?

.... (1 mark)

(b) Explain how a protein is made from a section of DNA.

....
....
....
.... (4 marks)

Score   /17

How well did you do?

0–8 correct   Try again
9–17 correct   Getting there
18–26 correct   Good work
27–33 correct   Excellent!

TOTAL SCORE   /33

For more on this topic
see pages 60–61 of your Success Guide

INHERITED DISEASES

A

Choose just one answer, a, b, c or d.

1 What is the name of the disease that affects the red blood cells?
(a) malaria
(b) sickle cell anaemia
(c) cystic fibrosis
(d) Huntingdon's disease   (1 mark)

2 Which of the following diseases affects the lungs?
(a) cystic fibrosis   (c) haemophilia
(b) cholera   (d) sickle cell anaemia
                                  (1 mark)

3 Which disease is caused by a dominant allele?
(a) bronchitis
(b) Huntington's disease
(c) sickle cell anaemia
(d) cystic fibrosis   (1 mark)

4 What are the symptoms of Huntingdon's disease?
(a) chest infections
(b) uncontrolled jerky movements
(c) difficulty breathing
(d) muscle pain   (1 mark)

5 Which of the following diseases is not hereditary?
(a) haemophilia
(b) cystic fibrosis
(c) leukaemia
(d) phenylketonuria   (1 mark)

Score   /5

B

Answer all parts of the question.

1 Huntington's disease is an inherited disease of the nervous system. The disease is caused by an allele H, which is dominant to the normal allele h.

(a) Give two possible genotypes of a person suffering from Huntington's disease

.... (2 marks)

(b) Fill in the spaces provided to complete the following punnet square diagram where the father is heterozygous for the condition and the mother is normal.

Father's genotype ....   Mothers genotype ....

Gametes .... , ...   Gametes .... , ...   (2 marks)

	H	h
h		
h		

(4 marks)

Phenotypes ...., ...   (2 marks)

Score   /10

C **These are GCSE-style questions. Answer all parts of the questions.**

1 Cystic fibrosis is an inherited disease that affects approximately 1 in 2,000 children born in Britain. The allele for cystic fibrosis c is recessive to the normal allele C.

(a) Give the genotypes of a person

(i) with cystic fibrosis ....

(ii) who is a carrier of cystic fibrosis ....

(iii) who is normal .... (3 marks)

(b) What are the symptoms of cystic fibrosis?

....

.... (3 marks)

(c) How does a person inherit the disease?

.... (1 mark)

2 The diagram shows a family tree

David ⬤ ──── Julie ⬤

⬤ Normal
◯ Sufferer
◍ Carrier of cystic fibrosis

Adam ◍   Thomas ◯

(a) What is the genotype of David and Julie?

.... (1 mark)

(b) What is the genotype of Adam?

.... (1 mark)

(c) What is Adam's phenotype?

.... (1 mark)

(d) What is the probability of Thomas

(i) suffering from cystic fibrosis?

.... (1 mark)

(ii) being a carrier of cystic fibrosis?

.... (1 mark)

Score /12

How well did you do?

0–6 correct   Try again
7–13 correct   Getting there
14–20 correct   Good work
21–27 correct   Excellent!

TOTAL SCORE /27

For more on this topic
see pages 62–63 of your Success Guide

MITOSIS

Choose just one answer, a, b, c or d.

1 Which process uses mitosis?
(a) growth
(b) formation of gametes
(c) movement
(d) respiration (1 mark)

2 How many cells does a cell produce during mitosis?
(a) 6   (c) 2
(b) 3   (d) 4 (1 mark)

3 What shape is the DNA molecule?
(a) round   (c) a double helix
(b) long and thin   (d) a single helix (1 mark)

4 How many chromosomes does a cell have before it divides in two?
(a) 92
(b) 46
(c) 23
(d) 42 (1 mark)

5 What type of reproduction is mitosis?
(a) asexual
(b) sexual
(c) human
(d) animal (1 mark)

Score   /5

Answer all parts of the questions.

1 (a) How many chromosomes in a normal human body cell?

.... (1 mark)

(b) How many chromosomes in a human body cell that has undergone mitosis?

.... (1 mark)

(c) How many cells does mitosis produce from one cell?

.... (1 mark)

(d) How do the daughter cells compare with the parent cell after mitosis?

.... (1 mark)

2 Complete the following diagram of a cell that has undergone mitosis.

(2 marks)

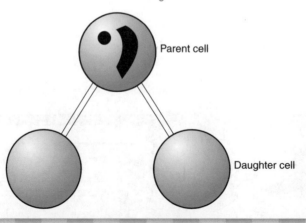

Parent cell

Daughter cell

Score   /6

C **These are GCSE-style questions. Answer all parts of the questions.**

1 **(a)** Describe what happens to chromosomes when a normal body cell divides.

.... (1 mark)

The diagram shows stages in the development of a human embryo.

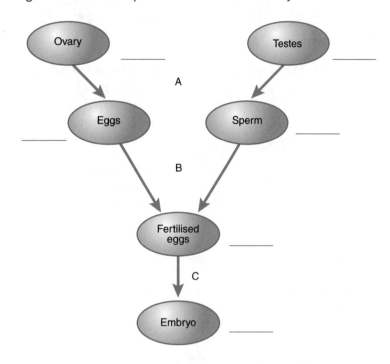

(b) Name stages   A ....

B ....

C .... (3 marks)

(c) Place numbers in the spaces provided to show the chromosome number of the
cells in the stages. (6 marks)

2 **(a)** When is the cell division process, mitosis, used in plant and animal cells?

.... (2 marks)

(b) Mitosis is an important process to commercial gardeners as it produces exact
copies of a plant. What is another name for mitosis?

.... (1 mark)

(c) Why do gardeners use mitosis to produce plants?

....

.... (3 marks)

Score   /16

How well did you do?

0–6 correct   Try again
7–13 correct   Getting there
14–20 correct   Good work
21–27 correct   Excellent!

TOTAL SCORE   **/27**

**For more on this topic
see pages 64–65 of your Success Guide**

MEIOSIS AND FERTILISATION

A

Choose just one answer, a, b, c or d.

1 How many chromosomes does a human cell have after meiosis?
(a) 23
(b) 92
(c) 46
(d) 21 (1 mark)

2 When does meiosis take place?
(a) making sperms
(b) growth of cells
(c) replacement of cells
(d) making skin cells (1 mark)

3 What are the chromosomes of a male?
(a) YX (c) XX
(b) XY (d) YY (1 mark)

4 What is a fertilised egg called?
(a) a fertilised egg
(b) an ovum
(c) a gamete
(d) a zygote (1 mark)

5 What is the diploid number of chromosomes in humans?
(a) 46
(b) 23
(c) 40
(d) 20 (1 mark)

Score /5

B

Answer all parts of the questions.

1 Fill in the gaps.

Meiosis is a type of cell division that takes place in the formation of .... Meiosis produces cells with .... the number of chromosomes as the original cell. Fertilisation restores the normal number of chromosomes to .... in a human. The female gamete is called an .... and the male gamete is a .... (5 marks)

2 (a) What chromosomes do the female ovary produce? .... (1 mark)

(b) What chromosomes are produced by the male testes? .... (1 mark)

(c) What is the probability of a couple having a boy as their first born child?

.... (1 mark)

(d) What is the visible difference between the X chromosome and the Y chromosome?

.... (1 mark)

Score /9

C These are GCSE-style questions. Answer all parts of the questions.

1 The diagram shows some possible combinations of egg and sperm at fertilisation.

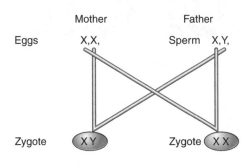

Mother   Father

Eggs   X,X,   Sperm   X,Y,

Zygote   X Y   Zygote   X X

Process 1   Process 2

(a) What do the letters X and Y represent?

.... (1 mark)

(b) What is a zygote?

.... (1 mark)

(c) What process produces the eggs and sperm?

.... (1 mark)

(d) How many chromosomes have the

     (i) eggs and sperm

     ....

     (ii) zygote

     .... (2 marks)

(e) Which of the above processes produce a

     (i) female ....

     (ii) male .... (2 marks)

2 What is the probability of a couple having a boy as their first child?
Use a punnet square in your answer.

....

....

....

.... (3 marks)

Score   /10

How well did you do?

0–6 correct   Try again
7–12 correct   Getting there
13–18 correct   Good work
19–24 correct   Excellent!

TOTAL SCORE   /24

For more on this topic
see pages 66–67 of your Success Guide

GENES, CHROMOSOMES AND MUTATIONS

A Choose just one answer, a, b, c or d.

1 Where are genes found?
(a) in the cytoplasm of animal cells
(b) on a chromosome
(c) in the vacuole of plant cells
(d) on a cell wall (1 mark)

2 How many genes are there for each feature?
(a) 2   (c) 4
(b) 3   (d) 6 (1 mark)

3 Which of the following could a cause of mutation?
(a) exercise
(b) eating
(c) radiation
(d) sleeping (1 mark)

4 Which of the following is not a base making up DNA?
(a) cytosine
(b) thymine
(c) adenine
(d) uracil (1 mark)

5 Can people inherit mutations?
(a) No, they just happen.
(b) Only if they occur in the body cells.
(c) Only if they occur in reproductive cells.
(d) You always inherit mutations. (1 mark)

Score /5

B Answer all parts of the questions.

1 The following table shows the relative amounts of DNA in cells in arbitrary units.

(a) How much DNA would you expect the following cells to contain

    (i) a sperm cell ....

    (ii) a fertilised egg cell ....

    (iii) a kidney cell .... (3 marks)

Cell	Amount of DNA
white blood cell	800
egg cell	400
red blood cell	0
skin cell	800
liver cell	800

(b) Why do the red blood cells contain no DNA?

.... (1 mark)

2 True or false?

	True	False
(a) Chromosomes are found in the nucleus.	☐	☐
(b) There are two chromosomes for each feature.	☐	☐
(c) All mutations can be inherited.	☐	☐
(d) DNA has four bases.	☐	☐
(e) A gene is a section of DNA.	☐	☐

(5 marks)

Score /9

C **These are GCSE-style questions. Answer all parts of the questions.**

1 Some scientists have investigated mutations in a species of blackfly. They exposed the blackfly to X-ray radiation. Here is a graph of their results.

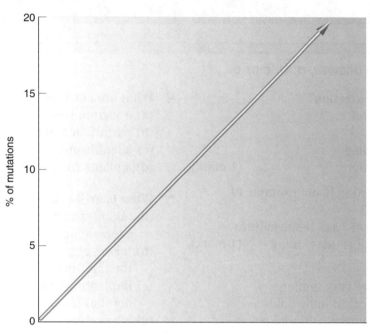

(a) What is a mutation?

....

.... (2 marks)

(b) What was the connection between the dose of X-ray and the percentage of mutations?

.... (1 mark)

(c) Name two other possible causes of mutations.

....

.... (2 marks)

(d) The blackfly produce offspring that did not show any evidence of mutation. Explain why.

....

.... (2 marks)

2 Explain the relationship between genes, chromosomes, DNA and the nucleus.

....

.... (3 marks)

Score   /10

How well did you do?

0–6 correct Try again
7–12 correct Getting there
13–18 correct Good work
19–24 correct Excellent!

TOTAL SCORE   /24

For more on this topic
see pages 68–69 of your Success Guide

SELECTIVE BREEDING

A

Choose just one answer, a, b, c or d.

1 What is artificial selection?
(a) natural selection
(b) evolution
(c) selective breeding
(d) selective variation   (1 mark)

2 Which of the following is not example of selective breeding?
(a) natural selection   (c) tissue culture
(b) artificial selection (d) cloning   (1 mark)

3 What is a clone?
(a) animals that are very similar
(b) genetically identical individuals
(c) plants with different coloured petals
(d) animals that look different   (1 mark)

4 What are cuttings?
(a) a section from a plant
(b) part of an animal
(c) a leaf from a plant
(d) a plants roots   (1 mark)

5 What is artificial insemination
(a) taking sperm from a male and an egg from a female, fertilising it, then putting it back
(b) taking eggs from a female, fertilising it then putting it back in
(c) implanting eggs from a female into another female
(d) implanting sperm from a male into a female   (1 mark)

Score   /5

B

Answer all parts of the questions.

1 Match the following terms with their definition.

artificial selection   inseminating a female animal with sperm

tissue culture   a term used for selective breeding

artificial insemination   breeding in desirable characteristics

selective breeding   growing plants from a plant cells   (4 marks)

2 (a) What are the differences between sexual reproduction and asexual reproduction?

....

.... (2 marks)

(b) What is the difference between artificial selection and natural selection?

.... (1 marks)

(c) What are the advantages of taking cuttings from a plant to produce new plants?

....

.... (2 marks)

Score   /9

C **These are GCSE-style questions. Answer all parts of the questions.**

1 An apple grower had a variety of apples in his orchard. One type was small but had a very nice sweet taste and another type was large but had a bitter taste. He wanted to produce a large apple with a nice taste.

(a) The apple grower used sexual reproduction to cross the variety of apples and produce seeds. Explain why he did this.

.... (1 mark)

(b) Describe step by step what he could do next.

....

....

.... (4 marks)

(c) Once the grower had his large tasty apples, he took some cuttings to produce more large tasty apples. What type of reproduction is this method?

.... (1 mark)

(d) Why did he use this method?

.... (1 mark)

2 (a) What is selective breeding also known as?

.... (1 mark)

(b) What are the problems with selective breeding?

....

.... (2 marks)

Score   /10

How well did you do?

0–6 correct Try again
7–12 correct Getting there
13–18 correct Good work
19 –24 correct Excellent!

TOTAL SCORE   **/24**

For more on this topic
see pages 70–71 of your Success Guide

CARBON CYCLE

A

Choose just one answer, a, b, c or d.

1 The amount of carbon dioxide in the atmosphere should?
(a) halve every year
(b) double every year
(c) stay the same
(d) triple every year (1 mark)

2 From what substance is coal formed?
(a) remains of plants
(b) remains of animals
(c) from rocks
(d) remains of animals and plants (1 mark)

3 How is carbon released into the atmosphere?
(a) feeding (c) photosynthesis
(b) decomposition (d) respiration (1 mark)

4 Which of the following processes removes carbon from the air?
(a) burning
(b) photosynthesis
(c) combustion
(d) respiration (1 mark)

5 What is the energy source for the carbon cycle?
(a) the Sun
(b) animals
(c) fossil fuels
(d) plants (1 mark)

Score /5

B

Answer all parts of the questions.

1 Fill in the gaps.

Carbon dioxide is recycled in nature. Plants absorb carbon dioxide from the air during the

process of .... Animals .... plants and incorporate the

carbon into their bodies. Animals release carbon back into the air during ....

Plants and animals produce .... and they .... Microbes

called .... decompose the waste material. The .... also

respire and release carbon. Animals and plants which do not decay eventually form

.... due to heat and .... These

.... release carbon dioxide back into the air when

they are burned. (10 marks)

2 (a) What conditions need to be present for decay to occur?

....

.... (3 marks)

(b) Approximately how much carbon dioxide is present in the atmosphere?

.... (1 marks)

Score /14

C **These are GCSE-style questions. Answer all parts of the questions.**

1 The diagram shows the carbon cycle.

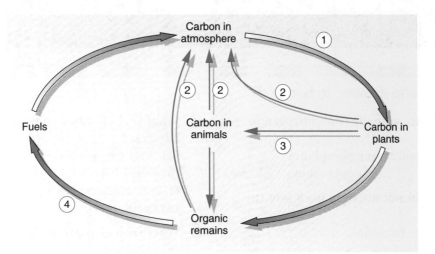

(a) In what form does carbon exist in the atmosphere?

.... (1 mark)

(b) What process is represented by the numbered stages?

1. ....

2. ....

3. ....

4. .... (4 marks)

(c) Describe how carbon in the atmosphere becomes carbon in the soil.

....

....

....

.... (5 marks)

(d) What organisms help in the process described in **(c)**?

.... (1 mark)

(e) What eventually happens to the carbon that does not get released back into the atmosphere by respiration?

....

.... (2 marks)

Score /13

How well did you do?

0–8 correct Try again
9–17 correct Getting there
18–25 correct Good work
26–32 correct Excellent!

TOTAL SCORE /32

For more on this topic
see pages 74–75 of your Success Guide

THE NITROGEN CYCLE

A

Choose just one answer, a, b, c or d.

1 What substance is made from nitrogen in the soil?
(a) nitrogen oxide   (c) phosphates
(b) nitrates   (d) potassium   (1 mark)

2 Which bacteria put nitrogen back into the atmosphere?
(a) denitrifying bacteria
(b) nitrifying bacteria
(c) nitrogen fixing bacteria
(d) decomposing bacteria   (1 mark)

3 What artificial process puts nitrates into the soil?
(a) fertilisers   (c) decomposition
(b) lightning   (d) nitrogen fixing bacteria
                                  (1 mark)

4 What sort of plants contain nitrogen fixing bacteria?
(a) flowering plants
(b) trees
(c) leguminous plants
(d) deciduous plants   (1 mark)

5 Where are nitrogen-fixing bacteria found?
(a) in the air
(b) in root nodules
(c) in plant stems
(d) in the seeds   (1 mark)

Score   /5

B

Answer all parts of the questions.

1 True or false?

	True	False
(a) Nitrifying bacteria change nitrates into ammonia.	☐	☐
(b) Denitrifying bacteria change ammonia into nitrates.	☐	☐
(c) Nitrogen fixing bacteria change nitrogen into nitrates.	☐	☐
(d) Plants and animals use nitrates to make proteins.	☐	☐
(e) Fertilisers add nitrates to the soil.	☐	☐
(f) Plants take up nitrates during photosynthesis.	☐	☐
(g) Animals receive nitrates through respiration.	☐	☐

AMMONIUM NITRATE

	True	False
(h) Denitrifying bacteria are present in waterlogged soil with no oxygen.	☐	☐
(i) Decomposers break down dead and decaying material into nitrates.	☐	☐
(j) Leaching washes nitrates into rivers and streams.	☐	☐

(10 marks)

2 (a) Why are leguminous plants such as beans and clover good for improving soil nitrate content?

....

....

.... (3 marks)

Score   /13

72

These are GCSE-style questions. Answer all parts of the questions.

1 The diagram shows a simplified nitrogen cycle.

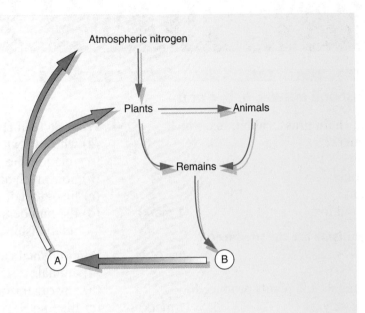

(a) Name the types of compounds found at stages

A ....

B ....   (2 marks)

(b) What type of bacteria turns compound B into compound A?

....   (1 mark)

(c) How do plants obtain compound A?

....   (1 mark)

(d) Give two ways that farmers can increase the amount of nitrates available to plants.

....

....   (2 marks)

(e) Explain how nitrates in animals and plants become nitrogen in the atmosphere.

....

....

....   (4 marks)

Score   /10

How well did you do?

0–6 correct   Try again
7–14 correct Getting there
15–22 correct Good work
23–28 correct Excellent!

TOTAL SCORE   /28

For more on this topic
see pages 76–77 of your Success Guide

FOOD CHAINS AND WEBS

A   **Choose just one answer, a, b, c or d.**

1 In the food chain grass, rabbit, fox, which
are consumers?
(a) fox only
(b) rabbit only
(c) the plant
(d) rabbit and fox   (1 mark)

2 Which organisms are the producers?
(a) plants
(b) animals
(c) both animals and plants produce food
(d) humans only   (1 mark)

3 What do we call animals that only eat meat?
(a) carnivores   (c) herbivores
(b) omnivores   (d) detrivores   (1 mark)

4 What do food chains show?
(a) who eats who in a simple feeding
relationship
(b) how much animals and plants eat
(c) linked feeding relationships
(d) the numbers involved in a simple feeding
relationship   (1 mark)

5 What do food chains always begin with?
(a) animals
(b) any organism can begin a food chain
(c) the Sun
(d) plants   (1 mark)

Score   /5

B   **Answer all parts of the questions.**

1 Read the following passage and use it to construct a food web.

In a pond, tiny green plants are eaten by tadpoles, water fleas and mosquito larvae. Water beetles and
water boatmen feed on the tadpoles. Small fish feed on the water fleas and mosquito larvae. Large fish
feed on the small fish, water beetles, water boatmen and tadpoles.

(5 marks)

2 What would happen to the water beetles if the tadpoles were all eaten by the water boatmen?

....

....

....   (2 marks)

Score   /7

C | **These are GCSE-style questions. Answer all parts of the questions.**

1 The diagram shows energy passing through a food chain

1,000 J	850 J	80 J

Sunlight   ➡   Grass   ➡   Rabbit   ➡   Fox

(a) How much energy is available to the rabbits?

.... (1 mark)

(b) How much energy is available for the fox?

.... (1 mark)

(c) Calculate the percentage of energy reaching the rabbits from the sunlight.

.... (2 marks)

(d) Not all of the energy from the rabbit passes on to the fox. Give examples of how the rabbit loses the energy.

....

.... (2 marks)

(e) Why do food chains rarely have more than four or five levels?

.... (2 marks)

(f) The grass does not receive all of the sunlight energy to be able to pass it onto the rabbit. Give two reasons why?

....

.... (2 marks)

Score   /10

How well did you do?

0–6 correct   Try again
7–12 correct   Getting there
13–17 correct   Good work
18–22 correct   Excellent!

TOTAL SCORE   /22

**For more on this topic
see pages 78–79 of your Success Guide**

PYRAMIDS OF NUMBERS AND BIOMASS

A

Choose just one answer, a, b, c or d.

1 Which of the following is not a way energy is lost in food chains?
(a) Animals and plants respire so lose energy
(b) Animals release heat energy during movement.
(c) Animals lose energy by keeping warm
(d) Plants moving (1 mark)

2 What does a pyramid of numbers show?
(a) the number involved in a food chain
(b) the mass involved in a food chain
(c) a linked food chain
(d) simply who eats who (1 mark)

3 What does a pyramid of biomass show?
(a) the numbers involved in a food chain
(b) the mass involved in a food chain
(c) a linked food chain
(d) simply who eats who (1 mark

4 What can be done to increase the efficiency of food production?
(a) have less stages in the food chain
(b) eat less plants
(c) eat less plants and meat
(d) do not produce as much food (1 mark)

5 Why do the numbers in a food chain get less at each level?
(a) loss of energy.
(b) the animals at the top can't eat more.
(c) animals only eat one thing.
(d) plants can't produce enough food. (1 mark)

Score /5

B

Answer all parts of the questions.

1 Read the following information and use it to construct a pyramid of numbers for the food chain described.

In a garden it was observed that 20 caterpillars were eating a rose bush, Later that day, five thrush birds were seen eating four caterpillars each. (3 marks)

2 The rose bush has a mass of 500 g, one caterpillar a mass of 4 g and a thrush 70 g. Draw a pyramid of biomass for this food chain. (4 marks)

Score /7

C These are GCSE-style questions. Answer all parts of the questions.

1 The food chain below shows the amount of biomass transferred to humans from 1,000 g of plant plankton.

    1,000 g   500 g   40 g   5 g

Plant plankton ➡ Animal plankton ➡ Mackerel ➡ Human

(a) Draw and label a pyramid of biomass for the food chain above.   (3 marks)

(b) What is biomass a measure of?

.... (1 mark)

(c) If the animal plankton decreased, what would happen to the

    (i) plants ....

    (ii) mackerel .... (2 marks)

(d) The mackerel numbers were falling, suggest two reasons why.

....

.... (2 marks)

(e) Suggest two measures that could be introduced to control the drop in numbers of mackerel.

....

.... (2 marks)

Score   /10

How well did you do?

0–6 correct Try again
7–12 correct Getting there
13–17 correct Good work
18–22 correct Excellent!

TOTAL SCORE   **/22**

**For more on this topic
see pages 80–81 of your Success Guide**

EVOLUTION

Choose just one answer, a, b, c or d.

1 Who put forward a theory of evolution?
 (a) Charles Newton
 (b) Charles Darwin
 (c) Nathan Darwin
 (d) Isaac Newton   (1 mark)

2 What provides the evidence for evolution?
 (a) living plants
 (b) living animals
 (c) fossils
 (d) mutations   (1 mark)

3 What does extinct mean?
 (a) no longer exist
 (b) never existed
 (c) only exist in the present day
 (d) Will always exist   (1 mark)

4 The three factors that need to be absent for fossils to form are?
 (a) light, cool and moisture
 (b) warmth, oxygen and light
 (c) moisture, warmth and oxygen
 (d) moisture, light and oxygen   (1 mark)

5 Which process causes evolution?
 (a) natural selection
 (b) reproduction
 (c) artificial selection
 (d) unnatural selection   (1 mark)

Score   /5

B

Answer all parts of the question.

1 There are two types of peppered moth, a light speckled form and a dark form. They are often used to provide evidence for evolution. Before the industrial revolution, all the moths found were light coloured.

(a) What caused the light-coloured moths nearly to die out?

.... (1 mark)

(b) Where were the light coloured moths still found after the Industrial Revolution?

.... (1 mark)

(c) How did the dark-coloured moths develop from light-coloured moths?

.... (1 mark)

(d) What is the name of the process of evolution that caused the dark moths to develop?

.... (1 mark)

Score   /4

C **These are GCSE-style questions. Answer all parts of the questions.**

1 The graph shows the relative number of different species of organisms present on the Earth from 500 million years ago to the present day.

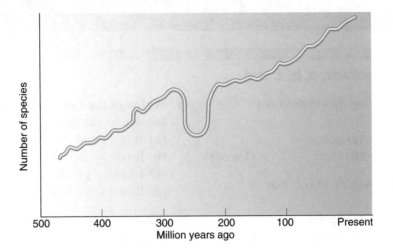

Million years ago

(a) What is the general trend from 500 million years ago to the present day?

.... (1 mark)

(b) Describe what happened between 300 and 200 million years ago.

....

.... (3 marks)

(c) Suggest a reason why species become extinct.

.... (1 mark)

2 **(a)** When animals and plants die, they usually decay. Occasionally, conditions for decay are absent and they can be preserved as fossils. State how the following organisms become fossils.

  (i) a mammoth in Siberia ....

  (ii) a mammal in the desert ....

  (iii) a fish in mudstone rock .... (3 marks)

(b) Evidence from fossils supports the theory of evolution. What is the theory of evolution?

....

.... (2 marks)

(c) What process causes evolution?

.... (1 mark)

Score   /11

How well did you do?

0–5 correct Try again
6–10 correct Getting there
11–15 correct Good work
16–20 correct Excellent!

TOTAL SCORE   /20

**For more on this topic
see pages 82–83 of your Success Guide**

ADAPTATION AND COMPETITION

A

Choose just one answer, a, b, c or d.

1 Which of the following do animals not compete for?
(a) light   (c) space
(b) mates   (d) food   (1 mark)

2 Which of the following do plants not compete for?
(a) food   (c) space
(b) light   (d) water   (1 mark)

3 Which of these is an adaptation of a polar bear?
(a) It produces little urine.
(b) It does not sweat.
(c) It had a thick coat.
(d) It can store water.   (1 mark)

4 Which of the following allows a camel to survive in the desert?
(a) It is a good swimmer.
(b) It has a thick coat.
(c) Its fur is greasy.
(d) It can store water.   (1 mark)

5 What determines whether an animal or a plant can survive?
(a) whether it can adapt to the environment
(b) the biggest animal
(c) the tallest animal
(d) which animal can eat the most   (1 mark)

Score   /5

B

Answer all parts of the questions.

1 Look at the picture of a cactus. Describe three ways in which it has adapted to live in the desert.

....

....

....

....

....

....   (3 marks)

2 In a community there are factors that prevent the numbers of plants or animals from growing out of control. Name three of these limiting factors.

....

....

....

....   (3 marks)

3 (a) What is a predator? ....

(b) What is a prey? ....   (3 marks)

Score   /9

C These are GCSE-style questions. Answer all parts of the questions.

1 The table shows the number of owls and mice in an area of woodland over a 6-year period.

	Owls (numbers)	Mice (numbers)
year 1	10	15
2	5	10
3	15	20
4	20	30
5	5	10
6	10	20

(a) Describe the changes in the populations of mice between 0 and 3 years.

....

....

.... (3 marks)

(b) Suggest two reasons why the numbers of mice fell between 3 and 4 years.

....

.... (2 marks)

(c) Why does the owl population fall between 4 and 5 years?

.... (1 mark)

(d) What would happen to the population of mice if the owls were to die out?

.... (1 mark)

(e) Explain why your answer to **(d)** would happen.

.... (1 mark)

(f) The population of owls and mice follow a cycle pattern. What is this pattern called?

....

.... (1 mark)

Score   /9

TOTAL SCORE   /23

For more on this topic
see pages 84–85 of your Success Guide

81

HUMAN INFLUENCE ON THE ENVIRONMENT

A Choose just one answer, a, b, c or d.

1 Eutrophication is the name of a process in which
(a) Animals thrive in good conditions.
(b) Algae grow rapidly.
(c) Algae slow down its growth.
(d) Plants do not grow at all. (1 mark)

2 Which of the following is a consequence of deforestation?
(a) more tree growth
(b) less carbon dioxide
(c) soil erosion
(d) more oxygen in the air (1 mark)

3 What are pesticides?
(a) They kill insects.
(b) They kill certain crops. (1 mark)

(c) They fertilise the land.
(d) They provide food for insects. (1 mark)

4 Which of the following causes eutrophication?
(a) shortage of plant life
(b) too much carbon dioxide in the air
(c) burning fossil fuels
(d) sewage entering lakes (1 mark)

5 What is intensive farming?
(a) producing more food on a piece of land
(b) No fertilisers or pesticides are used.
(c) Plants are grown organically.
(d) farmers working really hard (1 mark)

Score /5

B Answer all parts of the questions.

1 True or false?

	True	False
(a) Deforestation contributes to the Greenhouse effect.	☐	☐
(b) Eutrophication is a useful process in rivers, lakes and streams.	☐	☐
(c) Using fertilisers can lead to eutrophication.	☐	☐
(d) Organic farming uses manure as a fertiliser.	☐	☐
(e) An example of a pesticide is DDT.	☐	☐
(f) DDT kills unwanted pests and is of no harm to other wildlife.	☐	☐

(6 marks)

2 (a) What is deforestation? .... (1 mark)

(b) Explain how deforestation can contribute to the Greenhouse effect.

....

.... (2 marks)

(c) Name one other problem that deforestation can have on the environment.

....

.... (2 marks)

Score /11

These are GCSE-style questions. Answer all parts of the questions.

1 Farmers were having trouble with insects destroying their crop of wheat. They decided to use a species of wheat that was resistant to a large number of insects. The wheat had been genetically modified.

(a) Give two arguments for, and two arguments against, controlling insect pests in this way.

For ....

....

Against ....

.... (4 marks)

2 Students studying a stream near a pig farm noticed that there had been a leak of sewage. They also noticed that there were many plants growing on the surface of the stream.

(a) Explain what caused this increase in plant growth.

....

.... (2 marks)

(b) Explain as fully as you can why it is important to remove the plants quickly from

the stream. ....

....

....

.... (4 marks)

(c) What is the process called that you described in **(b)**?

.... (1 mark)

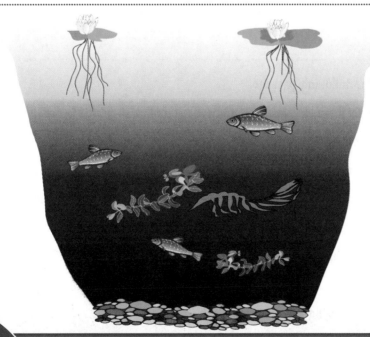

Score   /11

How well did you do?
0–6 correct Try again
7–14 correct Getting there
15–21 correct Good work
22–27 correct Excellent!

TOTAL SCORE   /27

**For more on this topic
see pages 86–87 of your Success Guide**

ACID RAIN, POLLUTION AND THE GREENHOUSE EFFECT

A **Choose just one answer, a, b, c or d.**

1 What is the main cause of acid rain?
(a) burning fossil fuels
(b) using fertilisers
(c) cattle waste producing methane
(d) chopping down trees   (1 mark)

2 What is the main gas that contributes to acid rain?
(a) oxygen   (b) nitrogen
(c) carbon dioxide   (d) sulphur dioxide
          (1 mark)

3 What is the main gas that causes greenhouse effect?
(a) carbon dioxide   (c) nitrogen oxide
(b) sulphur dioxide   (d) oxygen   (1 mark)

4 What causes holes in the ozone layer?
(a) carbon dioxide
(b) using cars
(c) chlorofluoro carbons
(d) burning fossil fuels   (1 mark)

5 Which of these is not a consequence of acid rain?
(a) damage to trees
(b) global warming
(c) pollution of lakes
(d) damage to trees   (1 mark)

Score   /5

B **Answer all parts of the questions.**

1 Explain how burning fossil fuels in one part of the country can still cause pollution in another part of the country.

....

.... (3 marks)

2 Fill in the gaps of the following passage.

Burning fossil fuels is the main cause of atmospheric pollution as it releases various gases into the air. Carbon dioxide contributes to the ....

Various nitrogen oxides and .... contribute to acid rain. The Greenhouse effect is causing .... The increase in gases is trapping the .... heat far more than normal and the Earth's temperature is rising. One way of reducing global warming is to use alternative .... sources and stop large-scale .... because trees absorb carbon dioxide. CFCs used in aerosols are also damaging the environment by causing the .... to develop holes. This means that harmful UV rays are reaching the Earth.

          (7 marks)

Score   /10

84

These are GCSE-style questions. Answer all parts of the questions.

1 The Greenhouse effect is due to a build–up of gases in the Earth's atmosphere.

(a) Name the two gases that contribute to the Greenhouse effect.

....

.... (2 marks)

(b) Explain why the Greenhouse effect is increasing due to

(i) the removal of tropical rain forests

....

(ii) rice fields

....

(iii) the burning of fossil fuels

....

(c) What does the term global warming mean?

.... (1 mark)

(d) State two effects that global warming will have on the Earth.

....

.... (2 marks)

2 (a) Fossil fuels have been burnt in Britain for many years. The effects are much greater now than many years ago. Suggest why.

....

.... (2 marks)

(b) Burning fossil fuels contributes to acid rain as well as contributing to the Greenhouse effect. Which gases cause acid rain?

....

.... (2 marks)

Score   /9

How well did you do?

0–6 correct Try again
7–13 correct Getting there
14–19 correct Good work
20–24 correct Excellent!

TOTAL SCORE   /24

For more on this topic
see pages 88–89 of your Success Guide

BIOTECHNOLOGY

A

Choose just one answer, a, b, c or d.

1 Which food substance is not produced by fermentation?
(a) bread   (b) pasta
(c) yoghurt   (d) beer   (1 mark)

2 Who discovered penicillin?
(a) Alexander Flemming
(b) Isaac Newton
(c) Louis Pasteur
(d) Charles Darwin   (1 mark)

3 Which gas mainly makes up biogas?
(a) oxygen
(b) nitrogen
(c) carbon dioxide
(d) methane   (1 mark)

4 What is the name of the vessel used in fermentation?
(a) a fermenter
(b) a fungusarium
(c) a microber
(d) a substrater   (1 mark)

5 What organism is commonly used in fermentation?
(a) viruses
(b) fungus
(c) small animals
(d) green plants   (1 mark)

Score   /5

B

Answer all parts of the questions.

1 True or false?

	True	False
(a) Bacteria help produce yoghurt.	☐	☐
(b) Penicillin is a bacterium.	☐	☐
(c) Mycoprotein is a meat substitute made from a fungus.	☐	☐
(d) In a fermenter the temperature has to always remain high.	☐	☐
(e) An example of a biogas is methane.	☐	☐
(f) Methane gas can be used as a source of fuel.	☐	☐

(6 marks)

2 (a) What is the name of the vessel that is used to produce useful substances from microbes?

.... (1 mark)

(b) During industrial fermentation many factors have to be monitored and controlled in order to produce a product cheaply and efficiently. Name three of these factors.

....

....

.... (3 marks)

Score   /10

C **These are GCSE-style questions. Answer all parts of the questions.**

1 In the vinegar-making industry there are some bacteria that can change the alcohol in beer into vinegar. The diagram below shows the equipment used.

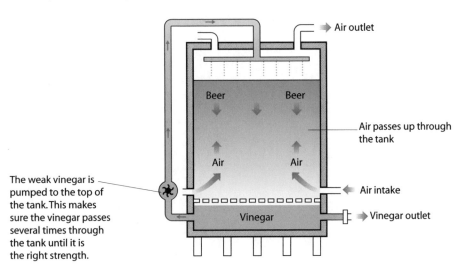

(a) What is the name of the equipment used to make vinegar in the diagram above?

.... (1 mark)

(b) The type of process used above is said to be continuous. Describe what this means, using the diagram.

....

.... (2 marks)

(c) Why does air need to be pumped into the vessel?

.... (1 mark)

(d) The content of the vessel becomes very hot. How is the heat produced?

.... (1 mark)

(e) How could the heat be controlled and made cooler and why is it important to do so?

....

.... (2 marks)

(f) Explain why the vessel needs to be kept sterile.

.... (1 mark)

(g) Suggest why pH is particularly important in this process.

....

.... (2 marks)

Score   /10

How well did you do?

0–6 correct   Try again
7–13 correct Getting there
14–19 correct Good work
20–25 correct Excellent!

TOTAL SCORE   /25

For more on this topic
see pages 90–91 of your Success Guide

MIXED GCSE-STYLE QUESTIONS

1 The diagram below shows the apparatus used to demonstrate breathing

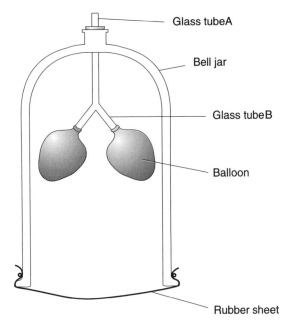

Glass tube A

Bell jar

Glass tube B

Balloon

Rubber sheet

(a) Which part of the body is represented by

(i) the balloon ....

(ii) the glass tube A ....

(iii) the glass tube B ....

(iv) the bell jar ....

(v) the rubber sheet ....   (5 marks)

(b) What happens when the rubber sheet is pulled down?

....

....

....   (4 marks)

2 The diagram below shows two types of cell division.

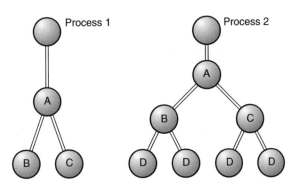

Process 1

A

B   C

Process 2

A

B   C

D   D   D   D

(a) The number of chromosomes in the original parent cell is shown. Give the number of chromosomes in cell

A ....   C ....

B ....   D ....

(4 marks)

(b) Which numbered type of cell division takes place during

(i) growth? ....

(ii) the formation of gametes? ....

(iii) repair of cells? ....

(3 marks)

(c) State two ways in which cell division 1 differs from cell division 2.

....

....

(2 marks)

3 In an experiment, red blood cells and plant cells were placed on a slide under a microscope. Water was added to both cells. The red blood cells burst but the plant cells did not.

(a) Explain why the red blood cells burst

....

....

....

(3 marks)

(b) Explain why the plant cells did not burst

....

....

(3 marks)

(c) What eventually happens to plant cells that lose water?

....

....

....

(4 marks)

4 The diagram shows an alveoli surrounded by a blood capillary.

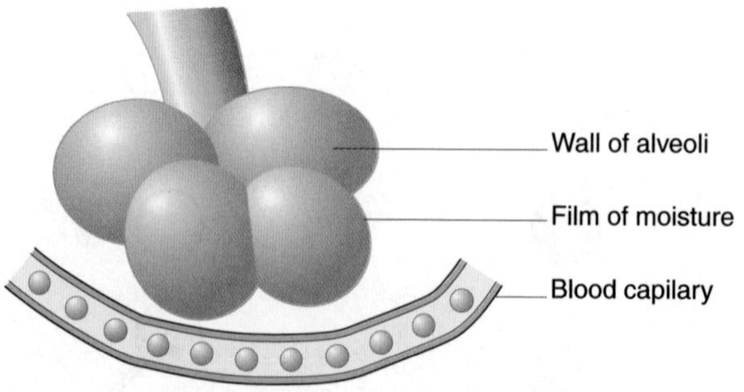

Wall of alveoli

Film of moisture

Blood capilary

(a) Where in the body are alveoli found?

....

(1 mark)

(b) Which gas passes from the alveoli to the blood?

....

.... (1 mark)

(c) Which gas passes from the blood into the alveoli?

....

.... (1 mark)

(d) Explain how the gas in (b) passes from the air in the alveoli into the blood.

....

....

....

.... (3 marks)

(e) Give three ways in which the structure of the alveoli is adapted for gas exchange.

....

....

....

.... (3 marks)

5 The diagram shows a capillary bed in a tissue

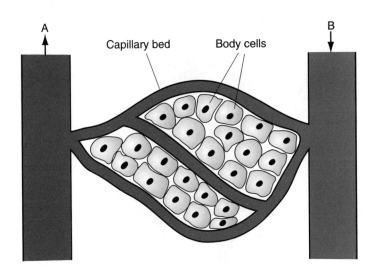

(a) Name a gas that moves from the capillary to the body cells.

....

.... (1 mark)

(b) What do the cells use this gas for?

....

.... (1 mark)

(c) Name two substances that pass in the opposite direction to the gas in (a)

....

....

....
(2 marks)

(d) State two properties of the capillary walls that allow substances to pass through easily.

....

....

....
(2 marks)

(e) Name the type of blood vessel labelled

   (i) A..

   (ii) B ....
(2 marks)

(f) Give the letter or name of the blood vessel that has brought blood at high pressure to the tissue.

....

....
(1 mark)

6 The diagram shown is of the heart and its associated blood vessels

(a) Name the blood vessels labelled

A ....   B ....   C ....

D ....
(4 marks)

(b) Match one of the letters or labelled parts on the diagram with each of the following.

   (i) the thickest walled chamber ....

   (ii) the blood vessel that carries blood from the lungs to the heart ....

   (iii)the chamber that receives blood from the body ....

   (iv)the chamber which pumps blood to the body ....

   (v) the blood vessel that carries blood to the body ....

(c) Which part of the heart prevents blood flowing backwards?

....
(1 mark)

7 The diagrams below show the cross–section of three types of blood vessels.

(a) Which diagram represents an

(i) artery ....

(ii) vein ....

(iii) capillary ....

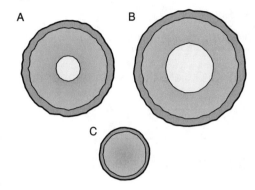

(b) Explain how arteries are adapted for their function.

....

....
(2 marks)

(c) Which of the three blood vessels contain valves and what is the function of valves?

....
(2 marks)

(d) What important functions do capillaries have?

....

....
(2 marks)

8 The diagram shows the equipment used to determine the energy content in two types of food. The results of the experiment are also shown.

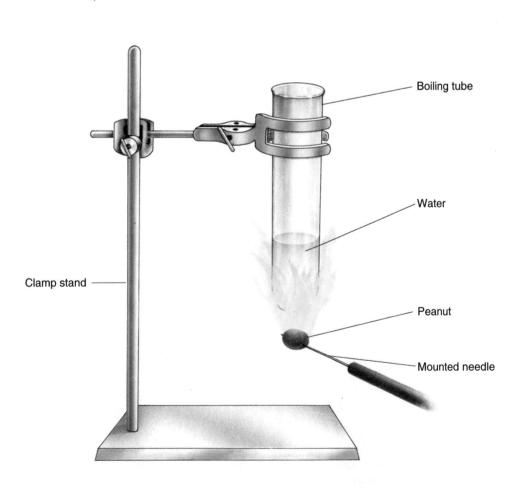

	Mass	Temperature of water before heating	Temperature of water after heating
Peanut	1 g	17°C	40°C
Popcorn	1 g	19°C	25°C
(amount of water = 20 cm³)			

(a) Calculate the rise in temperature of the water when heated by the peanut.

....

.... (1 mark)

(b) Calculate the rise in temperature of the water when heated by the popcorn.

....

.... (1 mark)

(c) Not all of the heat given off by the burning food heats the water, give two reasons why.

....

.... (2 marks)

(d) The amount of heat absorbed by the water is calculated using the following formula.
4.2 × amount of water × temperature rise = heat absorbed (J)
Calculate the heat absorbed by the water when heated by

(i) the peanut

....

(ii) the popcorn

....

(e) What is the relationship between the temperature rise and the energy content in food?

....

.... (1 mark)

9 The bar chart shows the daily amount of water lost by three organs in the body

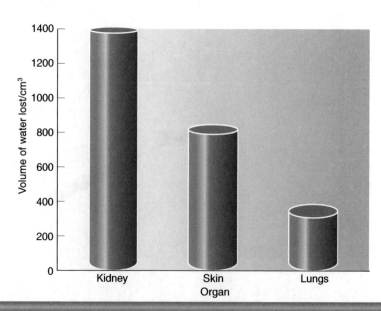

(a) What is the total amount of water lost each day?

....

.... (1 mark)

(b) What is the percentage loss of water by the skin and lungs? Show your working.

....

....

.... (2 marks)

(c) During summer the volume of water lost by the skin increases while the volume of water lost by the kidney decreases. Explain why

....

....

.... (2 marks)

(d) Explain why the amount of water lost increases during exercise.

....

....

.... (2 marks)

MIXED QUESTIONS-ANSWERS

1 (a) (i) the lungs

(ii) trachea

(iii) bronchi/bronchioles

(iv) the ribs

(v) the diaphragm

(b) volume increases, pressure falls, air is drawn in, balloons inflate

2 (a) A = 92 B = 46 C = 46 D = 23

(b) (i) 1

(ii) 2

(iii) 1

(c) 2 cells in process 1 4 in process 2
23 chromosomes in cells in process 2
46 chromosomes in process 1

3 (a) Water moves by osmosis from high to low concentration into the red blood cells which have no cell walls so they burst

(b) Water moves by osmosis from high to low concentration into the plant cell, the cell wall prevents it from bursting

(c) vacuoles shrink as water moves out; the cell becomes flaccid; the cytoplasm peels away from the cell wall; and the cell becomes plasmolysed

4 (a) the lungs

(b) oxygen

(c) carbon dioxide

(d) oxygen dissolves in the moisture; then diffuses through the alveoli and capillary walls; into the blood

(e) Large surface area, thin walls, moist lining, good blood supply (any three)

5 (a) Oxygen

(b) respiration

(c) waste and carbon dioxide

(d) thin and permeable walls

(e) A = vein B = artery

(f) artery/A

6 (a) A = vena cava B = pulmonary artery
C = aorta D = pulmonary vein

(b) (i) left ventricle

(ii) pulmonary vein/D

(iii) right atrium

(iv) left ventricle

(v) aorta/C

(c) The valves

7 (a) (i) A

(ii) B

(iii) C

(b) they have thick, muscular, elastic walls to carry blood at high pressure

(c) Veins, to prevent back flow of blood

(d) They deliver nutrients and oxygen to the body cells

8 (a) 23 degrees Celsius/23 °C

(b) 6 degrees Celsius/6 °C

(c) heat lost to the atmosphere, heat absorbed by the glass, not all food burns completely

(d) (i) $4.2 \times 20 \times 23 = 1932$ joules

(ii) $4.2 \times 20 \times 6 = 504$ joules

(e) The higher the temperature rise the greater the energy content in food

9 (a) 2500cm^3

(b) $100/2500 \times 100 = 44\%$

(c) increased sweating, water lost through skin increases, less urine is produced by the kidneys to compensate.

(d) increase in sweating and increase in breathing rate means more water lost via the lungs and skin

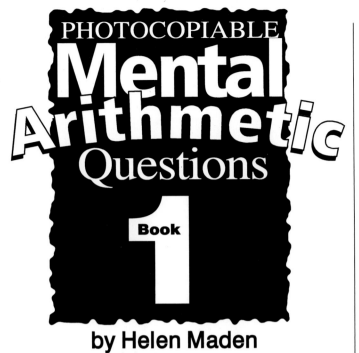

by Helen Maden

Mental Arithmetic Questions Book 1 is the first of a series of four books which provide a bank of easily accessible Mental Arithmetic Questions for use in a variety of classroom situations. It contains thirty different exercises which progressively get harder. Each exercise includes: Teacher Questions suitable for reading aloud, all answers needed and a photocopiable Pupil Answer Sheet with promts given where necessary.

Book 1 includes work from The National Curriculum Levels 2 and 3, mathematical problems using numbers up to 500 and concepts taken from The National Numeracy Strategy Key Objectives for Year Three.

Topical Resources publishes a range of Educational Materials for use in Primary Schools and Pre-School Nurseries and Playgroups.

For latest catalogue:
Tel: 01772 863158
Fax: 01772 866153

E.Mail: sales@topical-resources.co.uk
Visit our Website on:
www.topical-resources.co.uk

Copyright © 1999 Helen Maden
Illustrated by Paul Sealey

Printed in Great Britain for "Topical Resources", Publishers of Educational Materials, P.O. Box 329, Broughton, Preston, PR3 5LT by T.Snape & Company Ltd, Boltons Court, Preston, England.

Typeset by Paul Sealey Illustration and Design, 3 Wentworth Drive, Thornton, England. FY5 5AR.

First Published September 1999.
ISBN 1 872977 44 8

Contents

Teacher's Notes

How the Books are Organised

This book is one of a series of four. It contains thirty Mental Arithmetic exercises which use a wide mathematical vocabulary as advocated in The National Numeracy Strategy. Each exercise consists of a page of Teacher Questions together with answers and a photocopiable Pupil Answer Sheet complete with all necessary prompts. The book also includes a master for a Teacher's Record Sheet and a Pupil Record Sheet.

Each exercise has been designed to begin with three easier questions so that every child in the group will be able to achieve some positive results.

Repetitive questions allow the children to become familiar with a large variety of problems. To make the activities suitably taxing, the questions progress from easy at the beginning of the book to harder ones towards the end.

Book 1 includes work from The National Curriculum Levels 2 and 3, mathematical problems using numbers up to 500 and concepts taken from The National Numeracy Strategy Key Objectives for Year Three.

Book 2 includes work from The National Curriculum Levels 2, 3 and 4, mathematical problems using numbers up to 1,000 and concepts taken from The National Numeracy Strategy Key Objectives for Year Four.

Book 3 includes work from The National Curriculum Levels 3 and 4, mathematical problems using numbers up to 10,000 and concepts taken from The National Numeracy Strategy Key Objectives for Year Five.

Book 4 includes work from The National Curriculum Levels 3, 4 and 5, mathematical problems using numbers up to 1,000,000 and concepts taken from The National Numeracy Strategy Key Objectives for Year Six.

How to Use the Questions

The questions in this book could be used in a number of different ways including:

(1) As the basis of quick fire mental oral work to be used at the introduction of a mathematics lesson.

(2) As a Diagnostic Test to assess understanding and ability to solve Mental Arithmetic questions.

(3) As preparation for end of year SATs tests.

The exercises in this book may be used to suggest questions for use in the quick fire oral mental session found at the beginning of every numeracy lesson. One approach could be to teach and practice questions of a similar type to those found on the exercise chosen for that week and then use the exercise as an assessment test at the end of the week.

Using the exercises as a diagnostic aid would involve carrying out a test with the children, then to mark the work, identify common misconceptions and use this information to inform planning and subsequent teaching. The children could then be re-tested at a later date to assess improvements made.

If the exercises are to be used to prepare children for annual SAT tests, the teacher would read each question aloud twice and then count silently five, ten or fifteen seconds (depending upon the time indicated in the teacher questions) before proceeding to the next question. Alternatively, the teacher may prefer to have a stop clock on his/her desk to help judge accurately the length of time given to help solve each problem.

At all times children should be discouraged from using any aids such as scrap paper, calculators, rulers, mirrors, protractors etc.and positively encouraged to as often as possible complete numerical operations in their heads!

The Teacher's Record Sheet

A teacher's record sheet is provided in order to keep track of the progress of each individual child. Spaces are provided to record the score obtained on each test. This can be used to identify pupils who need extra support, or more challenging material which can be found in the subsequent books in the series.

The Pupil's Record Sheet

A pupil record sheet is provided which can be photocopied for each child. A simple way for them to record their results in each test would be to shade along each row up to the mark obtained on that occasion. These results could be then read as a real life bar chart.

Teacher's Record Sheet

Class _____   Date Started _____

Pupil's Name	Test 1	Test 2	Test 3	Test 4	Test 5	Test 6	Test 7	Test 8	Test 9	Test 10	Test 11	Test 12	Test 13	Test 14	Test 15	Test 16	Test 17	Test 18	Test 19	Test 20	Test 21	Test 22	Test 23	Test 24	Test 25	Test 26	Test 27	Test 28	Test 29	Test 30

3

Book 1 Test 1 Teacher Questions

No.	Question	Answer
	Ten Second Questions	
1	What is one less than four?	3
2	What is the number after six?	7
3	What is the total of six and one and ten?	17
4	What is six more than one?	7
5	Which number is larger, fifty or forty nine?	50
6	What is the next number in the following sequence: 2, 4, 6, 8, 10 ....?	12
7	How many days are there in a week?	7 days
8	There are ten marbles in a packet. Lisa takes one out. How many are left?	9 marbles
9	What is the next odd number after 13?	15
10	What number is missing: 10, 11, 13, 14 ?	12
	Ten Second Questions	
11	What makes the number ten? six and........... ?	4
12	How many ten pence coins make twenty pence?	2 x 10p coins
13	Look at the graph. Which are there more of, girls or boys?	girls
14	How many right angles are there inside this shape?	6 right angles
15	There are twelve birds. Two fly away. How many are left?	10 birds
16	Look at this amount. There are £4 and how many pence?	60p
17	What time does the digital clock say?	5 o'clock
18	What is the number shown by the arrow?	3
19	How many curved sides does this shape have?	2 curved sides
20	What is twenty six plus ten?	36

Book 1 Test 1 Pupil Answer Sheet

Name_____   Date_____   Total Score [   ]

Five Second Questions

(1) [   ]

(2) [   ]

(3) [   ]

(4) [   ]

(5) [   ]

(6) [   ]

(7) [days]

(8) [marbles   ]

(9) [   ]

(10) [   ]

Ten Second Questions

(11) [   ]

(12) [ten
           pence
           coins   ]

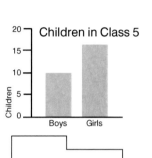

(13) [   ]

(14) [right
           angles   ]

(15) [birds   ]

(16) [p]   £4.60

(17) [o'clock]   `5:00`

(18) [   ]

(19) [curved
           sides   ]

(20) [   ]

5

Book 1 Test 2 Teacher Questions

No.	Question	Answer
	Five Second Questions	
1	What does two added to three make?	5
2	Write the number ten.	10
3	What is ten take away two?	8
4	What is the total of two and ten and one?	13
5	What is double two?	4
6	What number is missing: 22, 23, 25, 26 ?	24
7	What is the next even number after two?	4
8	What is thirty add thirty?	60
9	What is the next number in the following sequence: 21, 31, 41, 51 ....?	61
10	Find the difference between seven and one.	6
	Ten Second Questions	
11	How many sides does a pentagon have?	5 sides
12	Tick the coins that make fifteen pence.	10p and 5p
13	Write the number that is fourteen after ten.	24
14	What is half of forty?	20
15	Write two numbers that add together to make twelve.	e.g. 3+9
16	What time does the clock say?	5 o'clock
17	What is twenty nine plus ten?	39
18	Look at the graph. How many children go to school by car?	6 children
19	In a fruit bowl there are three apples, two pears and four bananas. How many pieces of fruit altogether?	9 pieces of fruit
20	How many straight sides does this shape have?	2 straight sides

Book 1 Test 2 Pupil Answer Sheet

Name_____   Date_____   Total Score [ ]

Five Second Questions

1 [   ]

2 [   ]

3 [   ]

4 [   ]

5 [   ]

6 [   ]

7 [   ]

8 [   ]

9 [   ]

10 [   ]

Ten Second Questions

11 [   ] sides

12 [(10p) (1p) (20p)   (5p) (2p) (1p)]

13 [   ]

14 [   ]

15 [   ]

16 [   ] o'clock

17 [   ]

18 [   ] children

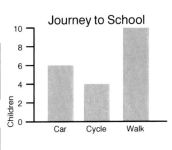

19 [   ] pieces of fruit

20 [   ] straight sides

7

Book 1 Test 3 Teacher Questions

No.	Question	Answer
	Five Second Questions	
1	What is the number before six?	5
2	What is six add one?	7
3	What is ten take away three?	7
4	Which number is larger, nine or twenty four?	24
5	What is a half of twelve?	6
6	What is the next number in this sequence: 14, 24, 34, 44, 54 ....?	64
7	There are ten green and yellow cars. If five are green how many are yellow?	5 yellow cars
8	What is the next even number after twelve?	14
9	How many days are there in a year?	365 days
10	What is the missing number: 25, 26, 28, 29 ?	27
	Ten Second Questions	
11	How many five pence coins make ten pence?	2 x 5p coins
12	Write the number that is twenty after thirty two.	52
13	Tick the shape with six sides.	
14	Look at this amount. There are £8 and how many pence?	23p
15	How many curved sides does this shape have?	2 curved sides
16	If James has 20p and spends 5p, how much does he have left?	15p
17	How many right angles are there inside this shape?	3 right angles
18	What is the number shown by the arrow.	8
19	Look at the graph. How many children like apples best?	7 children
20	What is forty two plus ten?	52

Book 1 Test 3 Pupil Answer Sheet

Name_____   Date_____   Total Score [ ]

Five Second Questions

7   yellow cars

9   days

Ten Second Questions

11   five pence coins

14   p   £8.23

15   curved sides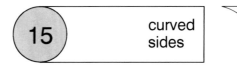

16   p

17   right angles

18

19   children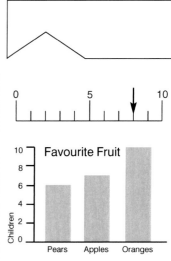

Book 1 Test 4 Teacher Questions

No.	Question	Answer
	Five Second Questions	
1	Write the number eight.	8
2	What is two less than six?	4
3	What is half of eight?	4
4	What is double ten?	20
5	What makes ten? seven and ....?	3
6	What is seventy take away ten?	60
7	What is the next odd number after nine?	11
8	What number is missing: 14, 15, 17, 18 ?	16
9	What is the next number in this pattern: 2, 2, 6, 6, 2, 2, 6 ....?	6
10	Find the difference between three and five.	2
	Ten Second Questions	
11	Divide this shape into quarters.	e.g.
12	There are six yellow balls, one red ball and two green balls in a bag. How many is that altogether?	9 balls
13	Look at this amount. There are £9 and how many pence?	16p
14	Write one o'clock on the digital clock.	1:00
15	How much is ten pence and five pence altogether?	15p
16	What is seventeen plus ten?	27
17	Tick the shape with three right angles.	
18	How many tens are there in thirty four?	3 tens
19	What is half of one hundred?	50
20	Look at the graph. Which colour is the favourite of most children. Green, red or blue?	Blue

Book 1 Test 4 Pupil Answer Sheet

Name_____   Date_____   Total Score

Five Second Questions

1

2

3

4

5

6

7

8

9

10

Ten Second Questions

11

12   balls

13   p   £9.16

14   :

15   p

16

17

18   tens

19

20

Favourite Colour

Book 1 Test 5 Teacher Questions

No.	Question	Answer
	Five Second Questions	
1	What is the number after four?	5
2	What is five added to five?	10
3	Which is smaller, forty six or fifty six?	46
4	What is one fewer than six?	5
5	What makes ten? four and ....?	6
6	What is the missing number: 51, 52, 54, 55 ?	53
7	Write the next number in this sequence: 51, 41, 31 ....?	21
8	There are ten birds and one flies away. How many are left?	9 birds
9	What is twenty add twenty?	40
10	Circle two odd numbers.	7 and 9
	Ten Second Questions	
11	How many two pence coins make four pence?	2 x 2p coins
12	Look at the graph. How many children's favourite meal is fish and chips?	8 children
13	Look at this amount. There are £3 and how many pence?	2p
14	There are twenty sweets in a packet. Jane eats five. How many are left?	15 sweets
15	Write two numbers that add together to make ten.	e.g. 5+5
16	Tick the shape with seven sides.	
17	What is ten more than twenty five?	35
18	How many straight sides does this shape have?	4 straight sides
19	What time does the clock say?	10 o'clock
20	Write the number that is twenty after seventy nine.	99

Book 1 Test 5 Pupil Answer Sheet

Name_____   Date_____   Total Score

Five Second Questions

1
2
3
4
5
6
7
8   birds
9
10   14   26   14   9   32   7   18

Ten Second Questions

11   two pence coins
12   children

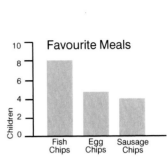

Favourite Meals

13   p

£3.02

14   sweets

15

16

17

18   straight sides

19   o'clock

20

13

Book 1 Test 6 Teacher Questions

No.	Question	Answer
	Five Second Questions	
1	What is the number before nine?	8
2	What is eight add one?	9
3	What is the total of four and one and ten?	15
4	What is double five?	10
5	What is two more than three?	5
6	How many months are there in a year?	12 months
7	What is the next number in this sequence: 14, 12, 10, 8, 6 ....?	4
8	What is the missing number: 7, 8, 10, 11 ?	9
9	What is twelve add twelve?	24
10	What is the next odd number after seventeen?	19
	Ten Second Questions	
11	What is half of twenty two?	11
12	How much is 2p and 5p altogether?	7p
13	There are nine acorns on a tree. Seven fall off. How many are left?	2 acorns
14	How many sides does a hexagon have?	6 sides
15	Look at the graph. How many children in this class have a brother?	8 children
16	What is ten add sixty two?	72
17	How many of these angles are right angles?	3 right angles
18	What is the number shown by the arrow.	4
19	Look at this amount. There are £7 and how many pence?	6p
20	Divide this shape into halves.	e.g.

Book 1 Test 6 Pupil Answer Sheet

Name_____   Date_____   Total Score

Five Second Questions

1

2

3

4

5

6 months

7

8

9

10

Ten Second Questions

11

12 p

13 acorns

14 sides

15 children

16

17 right angles

18

19 p   £7.06

20 ◯

Brothers and Sisters

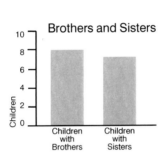

15

Book 1 Test 7 Teacher Questions

No.	Question	Answer
	Five Second Questions	
1	Write the number four.	4
2	What is ten subtract two?	8
3	Which number is larger, nine or twenty four?	24
4	What is half of four?	2
5	What makes ten? Three and ....?	7
6	In a class there are ten girls and ten boys. How many children altogether?	20 children
7	Circle the two even numbers.	12 and 14
8	How many seconds are there in a minute?	60 seconds
9	What number is missing: 17, 18, 20, 21 ?	19
10	What is the next number in this sequence: 50, 40, 30 ....?	20
	Ten Second Questions	
11	How many sides does a square have?	4 sides
12	Write two numbers that add together to make eight.	e.g. 1+7
13	Look at this amount. There are £11 and how many pence?	7p
14	Write seven o'clock on the digital clock.	7:00
15	How many ten pence coins make 30p?	3 x 10p coins
16	Look at the graph. How many children travel to school by car?	10 children
17	How many right angles are there in this shape?	0 right angles
18	What is ten more than thirty seven?	47
19	Divide the shape into quarters.	e.g.
20	Lisa had ten marbles. She gave three to Craig. How many does she have left?	7 marbles

Book 1 Test 7 Pupil Answer Sheet

Name_____   Date_____   Total Score

Five Second Questions

1

2

3

4

5

6 children

7 | 12 14 17 23 21 25 7 |

8 seconds

9

10

Ten Second Questions

11 sides

12

13 p   £11.07

14 :

15 ten pence coins

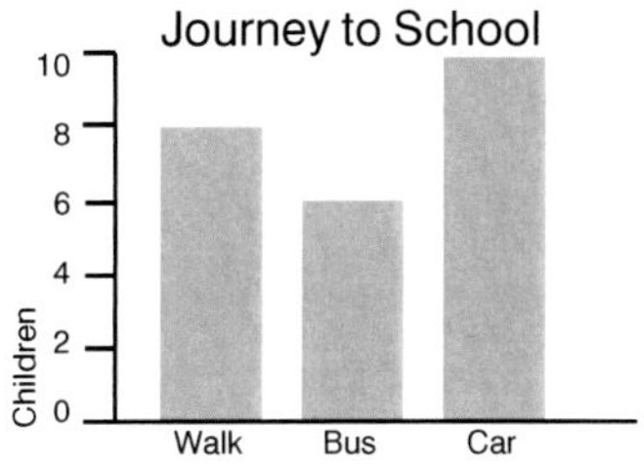

16 children

17 right angles

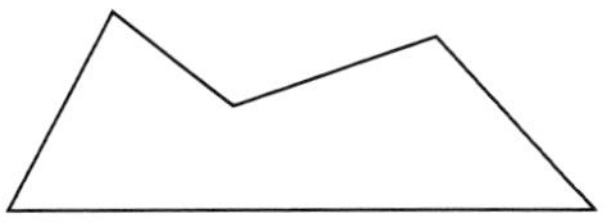

18

19 ◯

20 marbles

Journey to School

Book 1 Test 8 Teacher Questions

No.	Question	Answer
	Five Second Questions	
1	What is the number before two?	1
2	What is nine add two?	11
3	What is the total of ten and five and one?	16
4	What is eight fewer than nine?	1
5	What is double three?	6
6	What number is missing: 38, 39, 41, 42 ?	40
7	What is the next even number after eight?	10
8	A spider catches six flies, but one gets away. How many flies are left?	5 flies
9	What is twenty add twenty?	40
10	What is the next number in this sequence: 73, 63, 53, 43 ....?	33
	Ten Second Questions	
11	What time does the clock say?	9 o'clock
12	How many tens in fifty two?	5 tens
13	Find the difference between seven and three.	4
14	Write the number that is fifty after ten.	60
15	What is half of forty four?	22
16	What is ten plus twenty one?	31
17	Look at this amount. There are £19 and how many pence?	4p
18	How many five pence coins make fifteen pence?	3 x 5p coins
19	Look at the graph. How many children have pet rabbits?	4 children
20	Divide this triangle into halves.	

Book 1 Test 8 Pupil Answer Sheet

Name_____ Date_____ Total Score

Five Second Questions

① 1

② 2

③ 3

④ 4

⑤ 5

⑥ 6

⑦ 7

⑧ 8   flies

⑨ 9

⑩ 10

Ten Second Questions

⑪ 11   o'clock

⑫ 12   tens

⑬ 13

⑭ 14

⑮ 15

⑯ 16

⑰ 17   p   £19.04

⑱ 18   five pence coins

⑲ 19   children

Favourite Pets

(bar chart: Rabbits 4, Dogs 5, Cats 7; y-axis Children 0–10)

⑳ 20   △

Book 1 Test 9 Teacher Questions

No.	Question	Answer
	Five Second Questions	
1	Write the number nine.	9
2	What is two less than six?	4
3	What is ten take away five?	5
4	What is a half of fifty?	25
5	Which number is smaller, twenty three or seventeen?	17
6	A flower has five petals. Two petals are blown off. How many petals are left?	3 petals
7	Circle two even numbers.	12, 16
8	What number is missing: 26, 27, 29, 30 ?	28
9	How many minutes are there in an hour?	60 minutes
10	Write the next number in this sequence: 14, 24, 34, 44, 54	64
	Ten Second Questions	
11	There are four lorries, three cars and two buses on a road. How many vehicles is that altogether?	9 vehicles
12	Tick the shape with three sides.	
13	How many straight sides does this shape have?	2 straight sides
14	How many of these angles are right angles?	2 right angles
15	If an apple costs ten pence, how much would two cost?	20p
16	What is a quarter of twenty?	5
17	What is fourteen plus ten?	24
18	How much is twenty pence and ten pence altogether?	30p
19	Look at the graph. Which is the most common way of travelling to school?	bus
20	Tick the coins that make twelve pence.	5p 5p 1p 1p

Book 1 Test 9 Pupil Answer Sheet

Name_____   Date_____   Total Score [ ]

Five Second Questions

1

2

3

4

5

6   petals

7   12   7   16   19   9   17

8

9   minutes

10

Ten Second Questions

11   vehicles

12 △ □ ⬠ ⬡ ⬡ ⯃

13   straight sides

14   right angles   └ ⌐ ⌐ ∨

15   p

16

17

18   p

Journey to School

19

20 (5p) (20p) (5p)   (50p) (1p) (1p)

Book 1 Test 10 Teacher Questions

No.	Question	Answer
	Five Second Questions	
1	What is the number before 16?	15
2	What is eight add two?	10
3	Which number is larger, eighty or seventy nine?	80
4	What is ten fewer than sixteen?	6
5	What is a half of twelve?	6
6	Write the next number in the sequence: 90, 80, 70, 60	50
7	What is thirty add thirty?	60
8	Sam has nineteen peas on his plate. He drops one on the floor. How many does he have left?	18 peas
9	What is the next even number after six?	8
10	What number is missing: 28, 29, 31, 32 ?	30
	Ten Second Questions	
11	Which number is nine before forty five.	36
12	What is the number shown by the arrow.	1
13	In a street there are twelve houses. Four have to be knocked down as a new road is being built. How many houses will be left?	8 houses
14	How many sides does a triangle have?	3 sides
15	Look at the graph. How many more children are left handed than right handed?	4 children
16	How many two pence coins make 6p?	3 x 2p coins
17	What time does the clock say?	3 o'clock
18	What is ten added to eighty one?	91
19	How many curved sides does this shape have?	1 curved side
20	What is the number that is thirty after sixty six?	96

Book 1 Test 10 Pupil Answer Sheet

Name_____   Date_____   Total Score

Five Second Questions

1

2

3

4

5

6

7

8 peas

9

10

Ten Second Questions

11

12

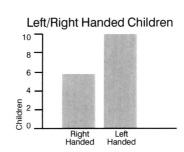

13 houses

14 sides

15 children

Left/Right Handed Children

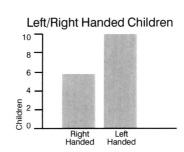

16 two pence coins

17 o'clock

18

19 curved side

20

Book 1 Test 11 Teacher Questions

No.	Question	Answer
	Five Second Questions	
1	Write the number one hundred.	100
2	What is one less then 10?	9
3	What makes ten; five and ....?	5
4	What is a quarter of 8?	2
5	What is twenty plus nine?	29
6	There are six hamsters in a cage. Three escape, how many are left?	3 hamsters
7	Circle two even numbers.	14, 28
8	What is the next number in this sequence: 23, 33, 43, 53 .....?	63
9	How many days are there in two weeks?	14 days
10	What number is missing: 51, 52, 54, 55 ?	53
	Ten Second Questions	
11	What is half of 80?	40
12	How many 10p coins make 50p?	5 x 10p coins
13	Write the number that is eleven before forty six.	35
14	Tick the shape with four sides.	☐
15	A chocolate bar costs 5p. How much would two cost?	10p
16	Jane has 50p and spends 40p. How much does she have left?	10p
17	How many right angles are there inside this shape?	5 right angles
18	Write two numbers that add together to make seven.	e.g. 3+4
19	Look at the venn diagram. How many children sing in the choir **and** go to football club?	7 children
20	Divide the shape into halves.	e.g. ☐

Book 1 Test 11 Pupil Answer Sheet

Name_____   Date_____   Total Score

Five Second Questions

1

2

3

4

5

6 hamsters

7 14   28   11   23   17   19

8

9 days

10

Ten Second Questions

11

12 ten pence coins

13

14 △ □ ⬠ ⬡ ⬡ ⯃

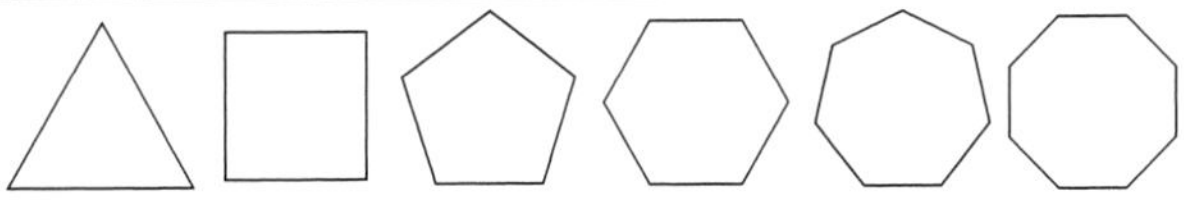

15 p

16 p

17 right angles

18

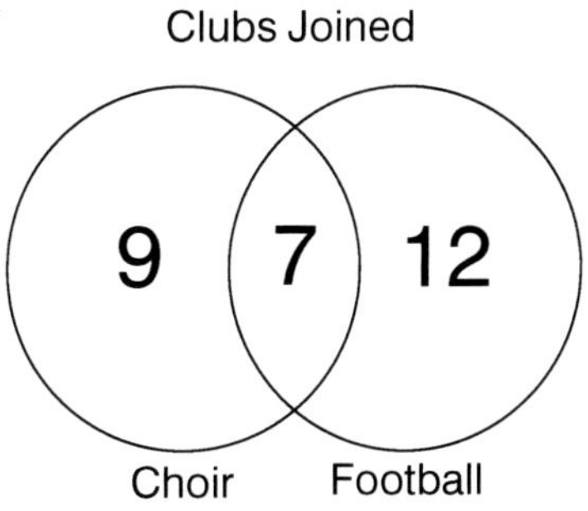

19 children

20 ☐

Clubs Joined

9 (7) 12

Choir   Football

25

Book 1 Test 12 Teacher Questions

No.	Question	Answer
	Five Second Questions	
1	What is the number after twelve?	13
2	What is eight subtract two?	6
3	What is ten take away five?	5
4	What is the total of 1 and 6 and 10?	17
5	Which number is smaller, forty six or twenty one?	21
6	What is fifty add fifty?	100
7	Two pears cost 10p. How much does one cost?	5p
8	What number is missing: 49, 50, 52, 53 ?	51
9	Circle the two odd numbers.	11 and 21
10	What is the next number in the sequence: 22, 32, 42, 52 ....?	62
	Ten Second Questions	
11	How much is 12p and 12p altogether?	24p
12	Tom has 10p, Edward has 3p and Harry has 2p. How much do they have altogether?	15p
13	Tick the shape that will not roll.	
14	Look at the graph. How many more children go to football club than netball club?	6 children
15	Write the number which is eleven before ninety one.	80
16	What time does the clock say?	e.g. half past 2
17	How many straight sides does this shape have?	3 straight sides
18	What is ten plus forty six?	56
19	What is the number shown by the arrow.	5
20	Write the number that is thirty more than 57.	87

Book 1 Test 12 Pupil Answer Sheet

Name_____   Date_____   Total Score

Five Second Questions

1

2

3

4

5

6

7   p

8

9   21   4   18   26   30   11

10

Ten Second Questions

11   p

12   p

13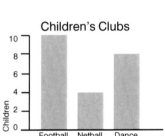

14   children

15

16

17   straight sides

18

19

20

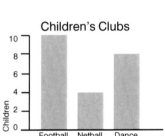

Children's Clubs

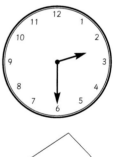

0 ↓ 10

27

Book 1 Test 13 Teacher Questions

No.	Question	Answer
	Five Second Questions	
1	What is the number before four?	3
2	What is eight add two?	10
3	What is a half of twenty?	10
4	What is ten fewer than thirteen?	3
5	What is double four?	8
6	What number is missing: 77, 78, 80, 81 ?	79
7	What is the next odd number after eleven?	13
8	Write the next number in this pattern 3, 3, 4, 4, 3, 3, 4, 4, 3, ...?	3
9	What is ten add ten take away two?	18
10	If Mary has 50p and spends 10p, what is her change?	40p
	Ten Second Questions	
11	What is the number that is eleven after seventeen?	28
12	Tim gets up at 7 o'clock. Sarah gets up 1 hour later. What time does she get up?	8 o'clock
13	Write 3 o'clock on the digital clock.	3:00
14	How many tens in nineteen?	1 ten
15	What is ten more than twenty one?	31
16	How many sides does a triangle have?	3 sides
17	Look at the venn diagram. How many children like chips?	15 children
18	Write the number which is nine before forty six.	37
19	How much are two 20p coins and one 1p coin altogether?	41p
20	Divide this shape into halves.	

Book 1 Test 13 Pupil Answer Sheet

Name_____   Date_____   Total Score [ ]

Five Second Questions

(1) [   ]

(2) [   ]

(3) [   ]

(4) [   ]

(5) [   ]

(6) [   ]

(7) [   ]

(8) [   ]

(9) [   ]

(10) [p]

Ten Second Questions

(11) [   ]

(12) [o'clock]

(13) [:   ]

(14) [ten]

(15) [   ]

(16) [sides]

(17) [children]

(18) [   ]

(19) [p]

(20) [▽   ]

Foods Eaten

2 (9) 6

burgers   Chips

29

Book 1 Test 14 Teacher Questions

No.	Question	Answer
	Five Second Questions	
1	What is the number before eight?	7
2	What is twelve added to one?	13
3	Which number is larger, sixty or fifty one?	60
4	What is ten take away nine?	1
5	What is a quarter of twelve?	3
6	There are eight trees in Mr Edward's garden. Three are blown down in a terrible storm. How many are left?	5 trees
7	What is the next number in the sequence: 41, 51, 61, 71, ...?	81
8	What number is missing: 63, 64, 66, 67 ?	65
9	What is twenty add thirty?	50
10	What is the next even number after fourteen?	16
	Ten Second Questions	
11	How many of these angles are right angles?	2 right angles
12	Tick the coins that make 6p.	2p, 2p + 2p
13	Look at the graph. How many more girls have a computer at home than boys?	3 girls
14	Write the number that is eleven after eighty three.	94
15	Tick the pentagon.	
16	What is the number shown by the arrow.	8
17	Sarah has twenty sweets. She eats thirteen. How many does she have left?	7 sweets
18	Divide this shape into halves.	
19	What is ten more than sixty?	70
20	What time does the clock say?	e.g. half past 11

Book 1 Test 14 Pupil Answer Sheet

Name_____ Date_____ Total Score ☐

Five Second Questions

1 ⬭

2 ⬭

3 ⬭

4 ⬭

5 ⬭

6 trees

7 ⬭

8 ⬭

9 ⬭

10 ⬭

Ten Second Questions

11 right angles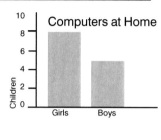

12 2p 2p 1p 20p 2p 10p

13 girls

Computers at Home (bar chart: Girls 8, Boys 5)

14 ⬭

15 △ ☐ ⬠ ⬡ ⬡ ⯃

16 0 ———↓——— 10

17 sweets

18 ⬭

19 ⬭

20

Book 1 Test 15 Teacher Questions

No.	Question	Answer
	Five Second Questions	
1	Write the number twenty six.	26
2	What is the number before sixteen?	15
3	What is the total of eight and one and ten?	19
4	What is half of six?	3
5	Which number is larger, twenty one or four?	21
6	Add thirty and thirty.	60
7	How many twos are in ten?	5 twos
8	What is the next odd number after three?	5
9	What is the next number in this sequence: 137, 147,157, 167 ....?	177
10	What number is missing: 48, 49, 51, 52 ?	50
	Ten Second Questions	
11	How many straight sides does this shape have?	6 straight sides
12	Write the number that is nine after thirty nine.	48
13	How many right angles are there in this shape?	1 right angle
14	What is ten more than fourteen?	24
15	How much is 20p, 10p and 2p altogether?	32p
16	Ken buys four tins of paint to decorate a room. He doesn't have enough so he buys two more. How many has he bought altogether?	6 tins of paint
17	Tick the cuboid.	
18	How many tens in sixty three?	6 tens
19	How many sides does a pentagon have?	5 sides
20	Look at the graph. How many children like apples or pears?	18 children

Book 1 Test 15 Pupil Answer Sheet

Name_____   Date_____   Total Score

Five Second Questions

1

2

3

4

5

6

7 two's

8

9

10

Ten Second Questions

11 straight sides

12

13 right angle

14

15 p

16 tins of paint

17

18 tens

19 sides

20 children

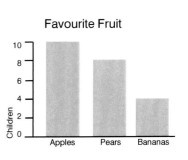

Favourite Fruit

33

Book 1 Test 16 Teacher Questions

No.	Question	Answer
	Five Second Questions	
1	What is two add six?	8
2	What is six subtract one?	5
3	Which is smaller, ninety one or eighty three?	83
4	What is one third of six?	2
5	Write the number one hundred and fifty six.	156
6	Add forty and forty.	80
7	There are nine books on the shelf. Three books are taken off the shelf. How many books are left?	6 books
8	Circle two even numbers.	2 and 6
9	What is the next number in this sequence: 164, 154, 144, 134 ....?	124
10	What number is missing: 85, 86, 88, 89 ?	87
	Ten Second Questions	
11	On a car park there are ten white cars, two red cars and three blue cars. How many cars altogether?	15 cars
12	Tick the shape that has four right angles.	▭
13	How many cms in 1 metre?	100cms
14	Tick the square.	▢
15	Tick the coins that make 25p.	20p and 5p
16	What is one hundred, add twenty, add seven?	127
17	Look at the venn diagram. How many children have a dog, but not a cat?	2 children
18	How much is 29p and 49p altogether?	78p
19	How many straight lines does this shape have?	2 straight lines
20	What is the number shown by the arrow.	10

34

Book 1 Test 16 Pupil Answer Sheet

Name_____

Date_____

Total Score

Five Second Questions

1

2

3

4

5

6

7   books

8   2   6   19   21   43   7

9

10

Ten Second Questions

11   cars

12

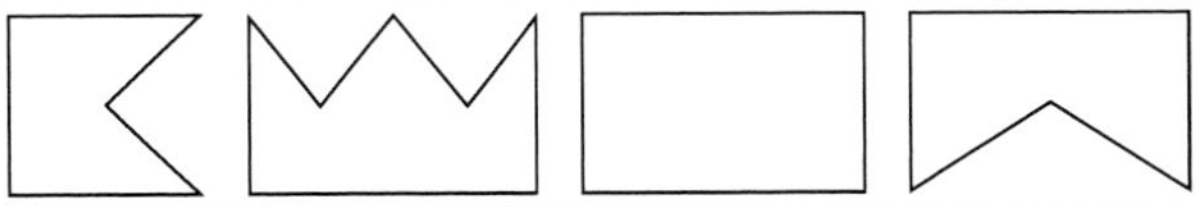

13   cm

14

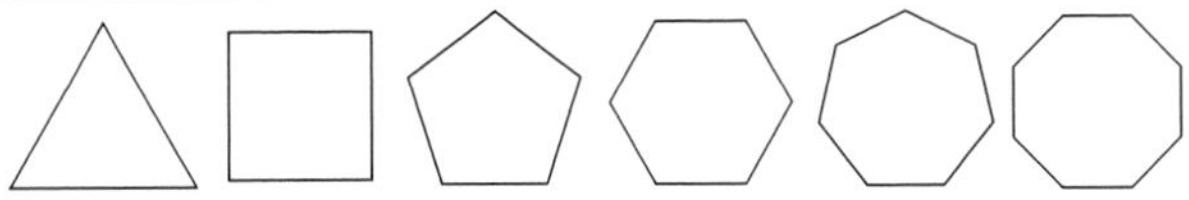

15   20p 1p 5p   10p 2p 1p

16

Children's Pets

2 | 3 | 6

Dogs   Cats

17   children

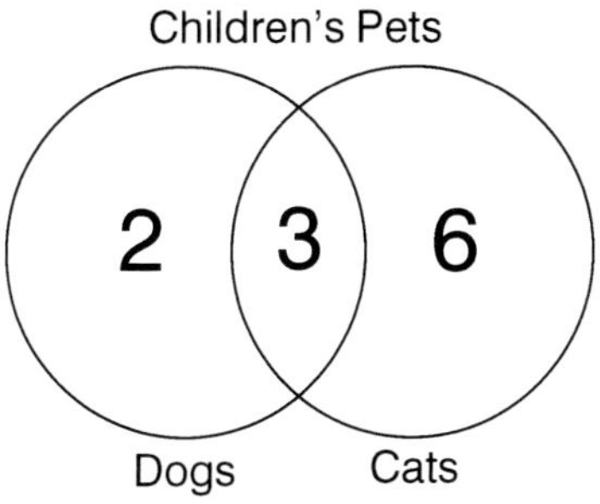

18   p

19   straight
       lines

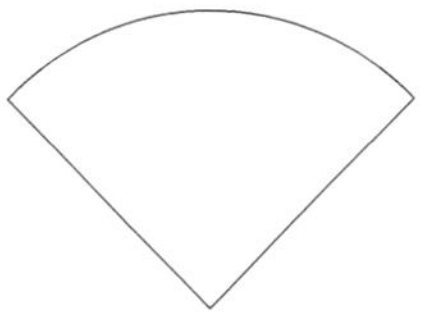

20

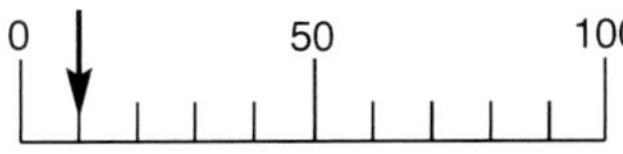

0   50   100

35

Book 1 Test 17 Teacher Questions

No.	Question	Answer
	Five Second Questions	
1	What is one less than five?	4
2	What does two added to ten make?	12
3	What is the total of 9 and 10 and 1?	20
4	What is a quarter of 4?	1
5	What is sixty plus eight?	68
6	What number is missing: 9, 10, 12, 13 ?	11
7	Circle two even numbers.	26 and 28
8	Find the difference between eight and two.	6
9	What is the sum of fifteen and fifteen?	30
10	What is the next number in this pattern: 31, 33, 41, 43, 51, 53 ....?	61
	Ten Second Questions	
11	How many 10p coins make 40p?	4 x 10p coins
12	Is 16 nearer 20 or 10?	20
13	What is half of eighty?	40
14	What is 20 add 40?	60
15	Write 6 o'clock on the digital clock.	6:00
16	Lucy has 20p. She spends 7p. How much change is she given?	13p
17	How many faces does a cube have?	6 faces
18	Write two numbers that add together to make 6.	e.g. 3+3
19	Look at the graph. How many more children like bananas than pears?	2 children
20	How many curved lines does this shape have?	3 curved lines

Book 1 Test 17 Pupil Answer Sheet

Name_____ Date_____ Total Score

Five Second Questions

1

2

3

4

5

6

7   26   13   57   19   28   21

8

9

10

Ten Second Questions

11   ten pence coins

12

13

14

15   :

16   p

17   faces

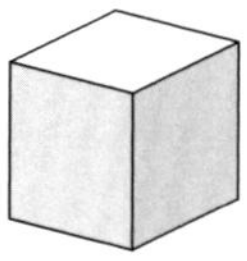

18

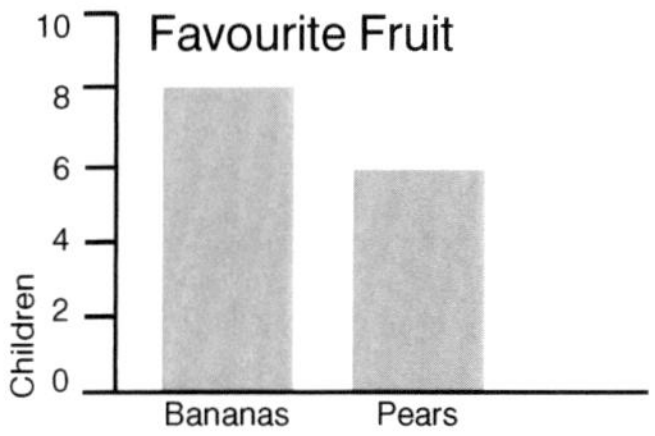

19   children

Favourite Fruit

20   curved lines

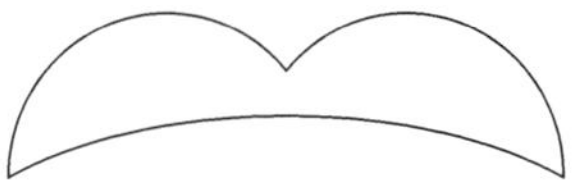

Book 1 Test 18 Teacher Questions

No.	Question	Answer
	Five Second Questions	
1	What is the missing number: 3, 4, 6, 7 ?	5
2	Write the number seventeen.	17
3	What is the number after 30?	31
4	There are six swans, one swims away. How many are left?	5 swans
5	How many twos are in six?	3 twos
6	What is the total of six, two and two?	10
7	What is twenty three add nine?	32
8	How many seconds are there in a minute?	60 seconds
9	What is double six?	12
10	What is the next number in this sequence: 160, 150, 140 ?	130
	Ten Second Questions	
11	If a pear costs 6p. How much do two pears cost?	12p
12	Add six and two, then half the answer?	4
13	Look at the graph on your sheet. How many children have a goldfish?	6 children
14	Sarah has 11p and spends 3p. How much does she have left?	8p
15	Is 26 nearer to 20 or 30?	30
16	What is the number shown by the arrow.	20
17	How many right angles are there in this shape?	3 right angles
18	What time is it?	3 o'clock
19	What is the number which is 10 after 60?	70
20	How much is 15p, 10p and 2p altogether?	27p

Book 1 Test 18 Pupil Answer Sheet

Name_____   Date_____   Total Score [ ]

Five Second Questions

1

2

3

4   swans

5   twos

6

7

8   seconds

9

10

Ten Second Questions

11   p

12

13   children

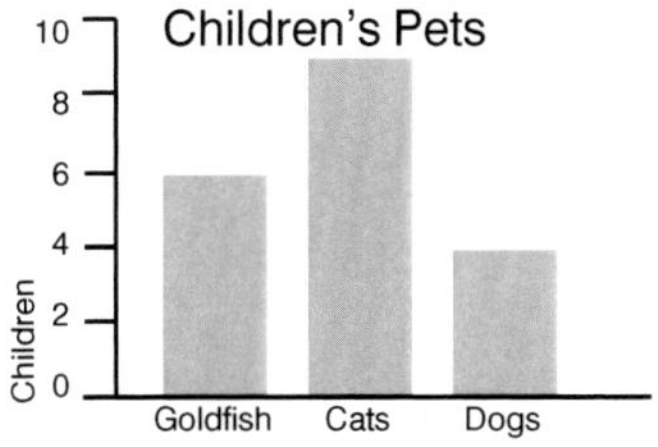

Children's Pets

14   p

15

16

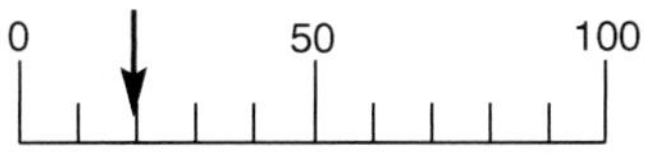

17   right angles

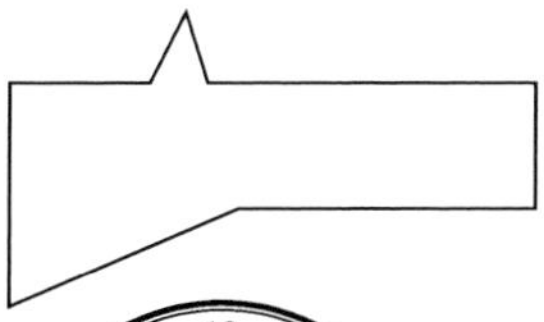

18   o'clock

19

20   p

Book 1 Test 19 Teacher Questions

No.	Question	Answer
	Five Second Questions	
1	What is the number after 12?	13
2	What is one less then nine?	8
3	What is double six?	12
4	What makes ten, one and .... ?	9
5	What is a half of fourteen?	7
6	Write the next number in the sequence. 100, 200, 300, 400 ....?	500
7	Circle two odd numbers.	17 and 21
8	If one car has four wheels. How many wheels do two cars have?	8 wheels
9	What number is missing: 17, 18, 20, 21	19
10	Add ten and ten then take away five.	15
	Ten Second Questions	
11	How many straight lines does this shape have?	1 straight line
12	What time does the clock say?	e.g. half past 2
13	Add 6 and 4, then half the answer	5
14	Tick the coins that make 30p.	20p and 10p
15	Tick the sphere.	
16	Look at the graph. How many more 7 year olds than 8 year olds are there in class 2?	6 more
17	Emily has twenty games. She doesn't use three anymore so she gives them to be sold at the school Christmas Fair. How many games does she have left?	17 games
18	How many right angles are in this shape?	0 right angles
19	How many tens in seventy two?	7 tens
20	What is the nearest ten to 37 - 30 or 40?	40

Book 1 Test 19 Pupil Answer Sheet

Name_____   Date_____   Total Score

Five Second Questions

1.

2.

3.

4.

5.

6.

7. 16 17 18 20 21 22

8. wheels

9.

10.

Ten Second Questions

11. straight line

12.

13.

14. 1p 20p 5p 2p 10p 1p

15.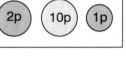

16. more

Children in Class 2

17. games

18. right angles

19. tens

20.

41

Book 1 Test 20 Teacher Questions

No.	Question	Answer
	Five Second Questions	
1	Write the number nineteen?	19
2	What is the number before eighty six?	85
3	What is seven fewer than eight?	1
4	How many tens are in sixty?	6 tens
5	How many millimetres in one centimetre?	10mm
6	A chocolate bar costs 8p. How much do two cost?	16p
7	What is twenty add twenty take away ten?	30
8	What is the next number in this sequence: 22, 21, 20, 19 ....?	18
9	What is the next even number after sixteen?	18
10	What number is missing: 88, 89, 91, 92 ?	90
	Ten Second Questions	
11	What is half of thirty?	15
12	Tick the rectangle.	
13	Lilly has 40p. She spends 2p. How much does she have left?	38p
14	What is the nearest 10 to 44 - 40 or 50?	40
15	Write two numbers that add together to make seventeen	e.g. 15 + 2
16	How many faces does a cylinder have?	3 faces
17	What is the number shown by the arrow.	50
18	How much is 39p and 49p altogether?	88p
19	Divide this shape into quarters.	e.g.
20	Look at the graph. How many children like to eat Mars Bars best?	10 children

Book 1 Test 20 Pupil Answer Sheet

Name_____   Date_____   Total Score

Five Second Questions

1

2

3

4   tens

5   mm

6   p

7

8

9

10

Ten Second Questions

11

12 ☐ △ ▭ ◯ ◇

13   p

14

15

16   faces

17

0 |||||↓||||| 100

18   p

19 ◇

20   children

Favourite Sweets

(Bar chart: Milky Way = 5, Kit Kat = 8, Mars Bar = 10, with Children axis marked 0, 2, 4, 6, 8, 10)

43

Book 1 Test 21 Teacher Questions

No.	Question	Answer
	Five Second Questions	
1	What is nine subtract one?	8
2	What is the number after forty six?	47
3	What is ten take away nine?	1
4	Write the number three hundred and seventy one.	371
5	What is one third of fifteen?	5
6	What is the next even number after eighteen?	20
7	What number is missing: 76, 77, 79, 80 ?	78
8	What is the next number in the sequence: 237, 247, 257 ....?	267
9	What is the next odd number after fifteen?	17
10	Ashley has ten goldfish, one cat and three rabbits. How many pets does he have?	14 pets
	Ten Second Questions	
11	Look at the venn diagram. How many children only play the piano?	2 children
12	What is 29p add 19p?	48p
13	Write half past eleven on the digital clock.	11:30
14	What time is it half an hour after 6:30?	7:00 / 7 o'clock
15	How many of these angles are right angles?	3 right angles
16	How many tens in eighty nine?	8 tens
17	What does the seven represent in the number 472? Circle the answer.	7 tens
18	How many straight lines does this shape have?	5 straight lines
19	A shopkeeper has twenty packets of cereal. He sells fourteen. How many does he have left?	6 packets
20	What is the number shown by the arrow?	18

Book 1 Test 21 Pupil Answer Sheet

Name_____ Date_____ Total Score ☐

Five Second Questions

1 ☐

2 ☐

3 ☐

4 ☐

5 ☐

6 ☐

7 ☐

8 ☐

9 ☐

10 pets

Ten Second Questions

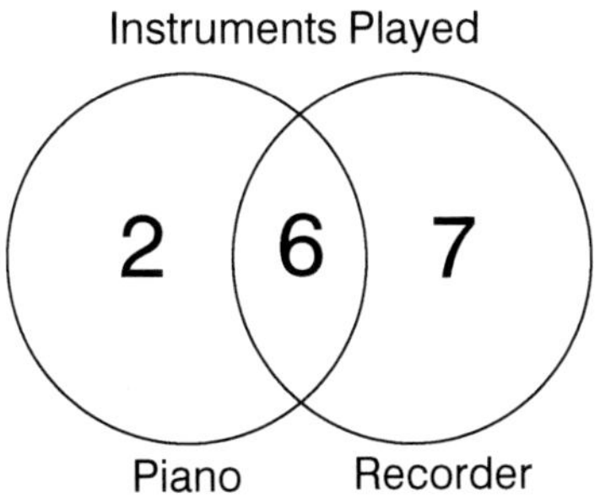

11 children

12 p

13 :

14

15 right angles

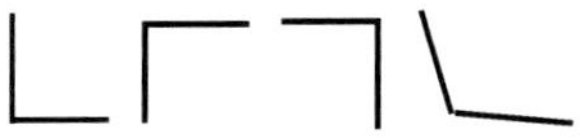

16 tens

17 7 hundreds   7 tens   7 units

18 straight lines

19 packets

20

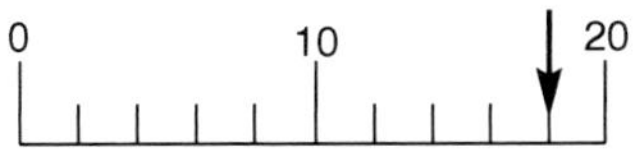

Instruments Played

2 6 7

Piano   Recorder

0   10   20

45

Book 1 Test 22 Teacher Questions

No.	Question	Answer
	Five Second Questions	
1	What is four add one?	5
2	Write the number twenty four.	24
3	Which is larger, forty three or sixteen?	43
4	What is eleven add forty six?	57
5	What is one tenth of thirty?	3
6	Write the next number in the sequence: 40, 39, 38, 37, ...?	36
7	What is ten add ten add twenty?	40
8	If Patrick has 10p and spends 2p, how much does he have left?	8p
9	Circle two even numbers.	2 and 14
10	What number is missing: 70, 71, 73, 74 ?	72
	Ten Second Questions	
11	How many faces does a cuboid have?	6 faces
12	There are twenty children on the bus. Eight get off at the first stop. How many are left on the bus?	12 children
13	Tick the coins that make 8p.	5p, 2p, 1p
14	Divide this shape into halves.	
15	What is twenty five more than 2.	27
16	What time does the clock say	e.g. half past 12
17	What is the nearest 10 to 37?	40
18	Write two numbers that add up to fourteen.	e.g. 1+13
19	How many right angles are there inside the shape printed on your sheet?	6 right angles
20	Look at the graph. How many more children prefer fish fingers to baked beans?	4 children

46

Book 1 Test 22 Pupil Answer Sheet

Name_____ Date_____ Total Score ☐

Five Second Questions

1

2

3

4

5

6

7

8   p

9   2   3   14   17   19   23

10

Ten Second Questions

11   faces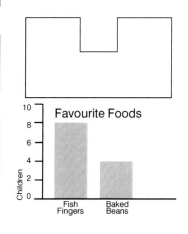

12   children

13   20p 1p 5p   10p 2p 1p

14

15

16

17

18

19   right angles

20   children

Favourite Foods
Bar chart, y-axis "Children" 0 to 10, Fish Fingers = 8, Baked Beans = 4

Book 1 Test 23 Teacher Questions

No.	Question	Answer
	Five Second Questions	
1	What is twenty two add two?	24
2	What is the number before sixty?	59
3	What makes ten; eight and ...... ?	2
4	What is the total of six and two and ten?	18
5	How many tens are in fifty?	5 tens
6	There are five people in a car. One is an adult. How many children are there?	4 children
7	What is the next even number after 30?	32
8	What is twenty add twenty, take away ten?	30
9	What number is missing: 95, 96, 98, 99 ?	97
10	What is the next number in this sequence: 404, 414, 424, 434 ....?	444
	Ten Second Questions	
11	How many 2p coins make 14p?	7 x 2p coins
12	There are 32 children in a class. 3 are away. How many are in school?	29 children
13	Tick the hexagon.	
14	There are thirty children in a class. Ten wear glasses for reading. How many do not wear glasses for reading?	20 children
15	What is a quarter of sixteen?	4
16	What is the number shown by the arrow.	12
17	What is half of twenty eight?	14
18	How many curved sides does this shape have?	2 curved sides
19	What is 43 more than 10?	53
20	Look at the venn diagram. How many children like coke, but not lemonade?	7 children

Book 1 Test 23 Pupil Answer Sheet

Name_____   Date_____   Total Score ☐

Five Second Questions

1 [   ]

2 [   ]

3 [   ]

4 [   ]

5 [tens]

6 [children]

7 [   ]

8 [   ]

9 [   ]

10 [   ]

Ten Second Questions

11 [two pence coins]

12 [children]

13 [△ □ ⬠ ⬡ ⬡ ⯃]

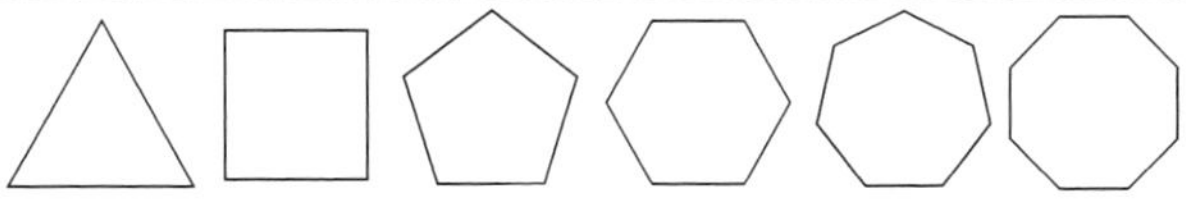

14 [children]

15 [   ]

16 [   ]   0 —————10—↓—20

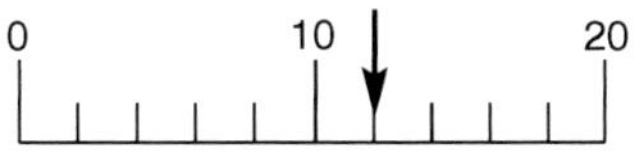

17 [   ]

18 [curved sides]

19 [   ]

20 [children]

Favourite Drinks

(7 (6) 0)

Coke   Lemonade

49

Book 1 Test 24 Teacher Questions

No.	Question	Answer
	Five Second Questions	
1	What is one less than six?	5
2	What is the number after fifty?	51
3	What is two fewer than six?	4
4	What is thirty plus eleven?	41
5	What is ten take away six?	4
6	What is the next odd number after twenty three?	25
7	There are 5 baby swings and 4 other swings in a park. How many swings altogether?	9 swings
8	What number is missing: 10, 9, 7, 6 ?	8
9	Add twenty and twelve.	32
10	Write the next number in this sequence: 1, 11, 21, 31, ...?	41
	Ten Second Questions	
11	What is half of twenty four?	12
12	In a field there are four brown horses, one white horse and one black horse. How many horses are there altogether?	6 horses
13	Write two numbers that add together to make twenty?	e.g. 10+10
14	Look at the graph. How many children like to play dominoes and snakes and ladders?	12 children
15	Tick the octagon.	
16	Tick two coins that make 3p.	2p and 1p
17	What time is it 2 hours after 6 o'clock?	e.g. 8 o'clock
18	Write half past two on the digital clock.	2:30
19	Divide this shape into halves.	
20	How much is 29p and 69p altogether?	98p

Book 1 Test 24 Pupil Answer Sheet

Name_____   Date_____   Total Score [ ]

Five Second Questions

1

2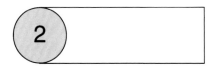

3

4

5

6

7 swings

8

9

10

Ten Second Questions

11

12 horses

13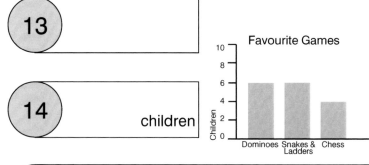

14 children

15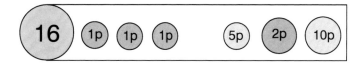

16

17 o'clock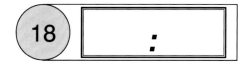

18 :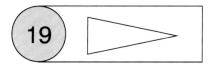

19

20 p

Book 1 Test 25 Teacher Questions

No.	Question	Answer
	Five Second Questions	
1	Write the number forty six.	46
2	What is six subtract two?	4
3	What is the total of two and two and two?	6
4	What is ten fewer than twenty?	10
5	Which number is larger, sixty or sixteen?	60
6	What is the number that is ten after forty six?	56
7	What is the next even number after thirty four?	36
8	What number is missing: 18, 17, 15, 14 ?	16
9	What is the next number in this pattern: 4, 14, 4, 14, 4 ....?	14
10	What is fifty add twenty two?	72
	Ten Second Questions	
11	The paper boy has twenty papers. He delivers 12 in Tinkers Road. How many more has he to deliver?	8 papers
12	What is a quarter of 20?	5
13	How much is 20p and 5p altogether?	25p
14	How much is 99p and 99p?	£1.98
15	Tick the circle.	
16	Look at the venn diagram. How many children like watching snooker?	8 children
17	What is the nearest 10 to 76?	80
18	What is the number shown by the arrow.	3
19	How many right angles are there in this shape?	2 right angles
20	Divide this shape into halves.	

Book 1 Test 25 Pupil Answer Sheet

Name_____ Date_____ Total Score

Five Second Questions

1.
2.
3.
4.
5.
6.
7.
8.
9.
10.

Ten Second Questions

11. papers
12.
13. p
14. £
15.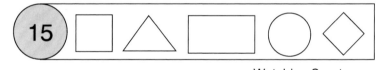
16. children
17.

Watching Sport

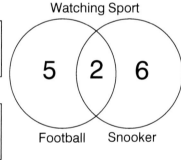

5   2   6

Football   Snooker

18.

0   10   20

19. right angles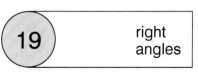

20.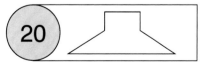

53

Book 1 Test 26 Teacher Questions

No.	Question	Answer
	Five Second Questions	
1	What is five add one?	6
2	What is nine subtract two?	7
3	What is the total of three and three and one?	7
4	What is double nine?	18
5	What makes ten; two and .....?	8
6	There are seven bananas in a bunch. Mother gave the twins one each. How many bananas were left?	5 bananas
7	What is the next number in this sequence: 472, 372, 272.	172
8	What is the next even number after thirty six?	38
9	How many fives are in ten?	2 fives
10	What is thirty add thirty take away ten?	50
	Ten Second Questions	
11	There are five petals on one flower and two petals on another. How many petals are there altogether?	7 petals
12	Look at the graph. How many children have red or yellow as their favourite colour?	6 children
13	Tick the shape that will roll.	
14	Write two numbers that add together to make thirty one.	e.g. 29+2
15	What is 25 plus 25 plus 3?	53
16	Write half past nine on the digital clock.	9:30
17	There are 32 children in a class. If 4 are away, how many are there at school?	28 children
18	What is half of sixty?	30
19	How many tens in sixty seven?	6 tens
20	How many straight lines does this shape have?	8 straight lines

Book 1 Test 26 Pupil Answer Sheet

Name_____   Date_____   Total Score

Five Second Questions

1

2

3

4

5

6   bananas

7

8

9   fives

10

Ten Second Questions

11   petals

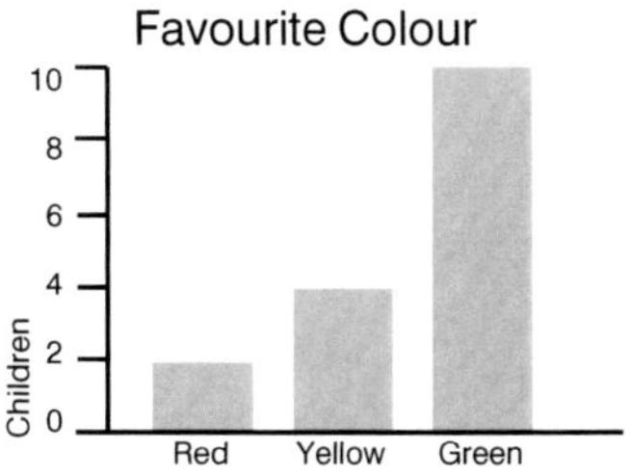

Favourite Colour

12   children

13

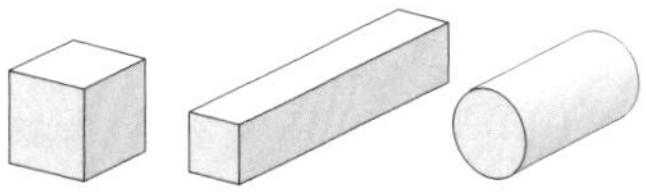

14

15

16   :

17   children

18

19   tens

20   straight lines

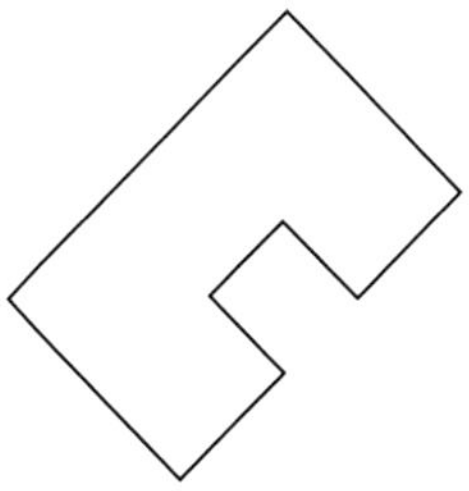

Book 1 Test 27 Teacher Questions

No.	Question	Answer
	Five Second Questions	
1	What is the number after fifty three?	54
2	What is one less than three?	2
3	What is seventy plus two?	72
4	How many 2p coins make 10p?	5 x 2p coins
5	Write the number four hundred and seventy two.	472
6	What number is missing: 74, 73, 71, 70 ?	72
7	What is twenty add twenty seven?	47
8	The journey is ten kilometres. The family have travelled six kilometres. How many kilometres are there left to go?	4 kilometres
9	What is the next number in this pattern? 26, 36, 26, 36	26
10	Circle two even numbers.	30 and 46
	Ten Second Questions	
11	What is four hundred add forty add nine?	449
12	What is one fifth of twenty?	4
13	What is the nearest 10 to 53?	50
14	How many right angles are inside this shape?	2 right angles
15	A car has four wheels, a bicycle has two wheels and a van has ten wheels. How many wheels altogether?	16 wheels
16	Look at the graph. How many children have a brother?	7 children
17	What is the number shown by the arrow.	10
18	What time does the clock say?	e.g. half past 10
19	How much is 3 lots of 99p?	£2.97
20	Divide this shape into quarters.	e.g.

Book 1 Test 27 Pupil Answer Sheet

Name_____   Date_____   Total Score

Five Second Questions

1.

2.

3.

4.   two pence coins

5.

6.

7.

8.   kilometres

9.

10.   17   29   46   23   30   21

Ten Second Questions

11.

12.

13.

14.   right angles

15.   wheels

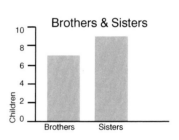

16.   children

17.

18.

19. £

20.

Book 1 Test 28 Teacher Questions

No.	Question	Answer
	Five Second Questions	
1	What is the number before ninety two?	91
2	What is the number after sixty three?	64
3	What is the total of six and six and one?	13
4	What is ten take away four?	6
5	Write the number three hundred and six.	306
6	What is the next odd number after twenty five?	27
7	I have 10 pennies in my pocket. Eight fall through a hole. How many are left?	2 pennies
8	What number is missing: 92, 91, 89, 88 ?	90
9	Circle two even numbers.	6 and 52
10	Add thirty and thirty seven.	67
	Ten Second Questions	
11	How many curved lines are there in this shape?	1 curved line
12	There are nine monkeys in a zoo. Five escape. How many are left?	4 monkeys
13	Tick the shape with six faces.	
14	How much is 20p, 20p and 5p altogether?	45p
15	Look at the venn diagram. How many children have a brother and a sister?	9 children
16	What time is it 6 hours after 2 o'clock?	8 o'clock
17	What does the one represent in 301? Circle the correct answer.	1 unit
18	What is the number shown by the arrow.	6
19	What is the nearest 10 to 74?	70
20	What is half of forty six?	23

Book 1 Test 28 Pupil Answer Sheet

Name_____   Date_____   Total Score

Five Second Questions

1 [ ]

2 [ ]

3 [ ]

4 [ ]

5 [ ]

6 [ ]

7 [pennies]

8 [ ]

9 [17   6   29   7   52   17]

10 [ ]

Ten Second Questions

11 [curved line]

12 [monkeys]

13 [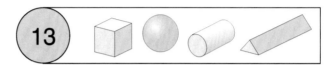]

14 [p]

Relations

15 [children]   6 9 7
Brother   Sister

16 [o'clock]

17 [1 hundred   1 ten   1 unit]

18 [ ]   0 ↓ 20

19 [ ]

20 [ ]

Book 1 Test 29 Teacher Questions

No.	Question	Answer
	Five Second Questions	
1	What is three added to one?	4
2	What is the number before twenty seven?	26
3	What is ten take away ten?	0
4	Write the number four hundred and three.	403
5	What is fifty six add nine?	65
6	What is the next number in this sequence: 26, 24, 22, 20 ....?	18
7	Find the difference between seventeen and ten.	7
8	Add forty and forty seven.	87
9	What number is missing: 81, 80, 78, 77 ?	79
10	What is the next even number after 40?	42
	Ten Second Questions	
11	Look at the graph. How many more children walk to school than ride in a car?	8 children
12	There are twelve biscuits on a plate. The children eat five, how many are left?	7 biscuits
13	Tick the shape with only two right angles.	
14	Write two numbers that add together to make forty-one?	e.g, 40 + 1
15	How much is 4 lots of 99p?	£3.96
16	What is the nearest 10 to 46?	50
17	Write half past eight on the digital clock.	8:30
18	Tick two coins that make 30p.	20p, 10p
19	What is five hundred add sixty add seven?	567
20	Divide this shape into halves.	e.g.

Book 1 Test 29 Pupil Answer Sheet

Name_____   Date_____   Total Score

Five Second Questions

1

2

3

4

5

6

7

8

9

10

Ten Second Questions

11 children

12 biscuits

13

14

15 £

16

17 :

18 20p 20p 1p 5p 2p 10p

19

20

Journey to School

Book 1 Test 30 Teacher Questions

No.	Question	Answer
	Five Second Questions	
1	What is ten subtract one?	9
2	What is the number after twenty nine?	30
3	Which is smaller, sixty or twenty four?	24
4	What is the total of ten and ten and five?	25
5	What is ten take away nothing?	10
6	How many fives in fifteen?	3 fives
7	What number is missing: 100, 99, 97, 96	98
8	If a child has 6 buttons on the front of his shirt and one on each cuff. How many buttons are there on his shirt altogether?	8 buttons
9	What is the next number in this sequence: 7, 6, 5	4
10	What is the next odd number after twenty seven?	29
	Ten Second Questions	
11	What is 59p add 29p?	88p
12	Divide this shape into halves.	e.g.
13	How many tens in twenty six?	2 tens
14	What time does the clock say?	e.g. half past 6
15	What is half of eighty eight?	44
16	In a street there are ten red doors, three blue doors and two yellow doors. How many doors altogether in the street?	15 doors
17	Tick the shape with three faces.	
18	What is the number shown by the arrow.	4
19	Look at the graph. How many children like music or maths best?	14 children
20	What is the nearest 10 to 92?	90

Book 1 Test 30 Pupil Answer Sheet

Name_____   Date_____   Total Score

Five Second Questions

Ten Second Questions

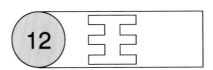

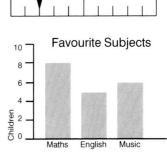

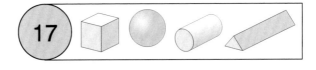

Pupil Record Sheet

Name_____

Colour in the boxes up to the correct score for each test.

	1	2	3	4	5	6	7	8	9	10	11	12	13	14	15	16	17	18	19	20
Test 1																				
Test 2																				
Test 3																				
Test 4																				
Test 5																				
Test 6																				
Test 7																				
Test 8																				
Test 9																				
Test 10																				
Test 11																				
Test 12																				
Test 13																				
Test 14																				
Test 15																				
Test 16																				
Test 17																				
Test 18																				
Test 19																				
Test 20																				
Test 21																				
Test 22																				
Test 23																				
Test 24																				
Test 25																				
Test 26																				
Test 27																				
Test 28																				
Test 29																				
Test 30	1	2	3	4	5	6	7	8	9	10	11	12	13	14	15	16	17	18	19	20